How to Get A's in High
Science is a book that fills
learning. The gap is twofold.

First, students do not have knowledge of what these courses are truly about prior to taking them. This book provides an easy to understand overview of each subject so the student will know what the subject is about in class from day one. Even during the course, this book would be valuable because it gives the student a total picture, which makes learning in the classroom easier.

Each subject is a chapter in the book and is a mini course in itself. In addition, there are just the right amount of problems and solutions provided to orient the student for the course.

Second, the summer prior to taking the six math and science courses (algebra, geometry, chemistry, physics, trigonometry, and calculus) is a gap in itself. Students have forgotten their previous math to some degree over the summer and have gotten out of the study habit. Each subject would only require about a half hour per day over a two week period to learn, but the problems should be gone over again and again.

Football players practice football in the summer to get a jump start on the game in the fall. This book does the same thing for each course. This book is like getting a 10 minute head start in a 5 k race.

In addition, there is a method revealed in the book that will truly show students how to get

the most out of their study time and classroom learning experience towards obtaining that A.

This book is also ideal for parents who feel inadequate in these subjects. This short course will provide a parent with a solid understanding of the subjects so they can help their child and at the same time help themselves.

Publisher: 4lini Publishing; Alabama.
Printed in the United States of America
4linipublishing@charter.net

Second Printing

ISBN: 978-0-615-98851-1

Table of Contents

Purpose of this Book

The United States has fallen behind in Math and Science to most countries in the world. We are below average in the testing scores in these subjects. Countries like Viet Nam, Ireland, and Poland beat us. In fact out of 65 countries, we ranked 36th in math and 28th in Science. So, 35 countries beat us in math and 27 in science. That is no way to remain competitive in the world. It is well known that improved math and science education increases jobs. This was clearly pointed out in U.S. News Weekly in an article by Mortimer B. Zuckerman titled "Why Math and Science Education Means More Jobs."[1]

The purpose of this book is to accomplish two objectives. First, the purpose is to provide a vehicle (this book) to give students a head start when they enter high school and as they take each math and science course. This book provides a means to "hit the ground running" from the first day of school. If you know where you are going, you are more likely to get there. I have basically compressed a year's worth of material into a short easy to understand reading with appropriate problems to give the student a jump start in math and science..

Getting a jump start will make it easier to learn and succeed. Plus this book provides a method to provide the student with a process that will virtually guarantee an A in the course if he or she follows the method as outlined for each subject. It would be equivalent to running a 5k race with a 10 minute head start and then having a greater speed in the race as well. So you would start off sooner and go faster. Unbeatable!!

This book is designed to provide just the right amount of material to keep the student's attention without overwhelming him or her with too much material. If someone gives you a map and points out where you are and where you need to go and shows you the route, it is a great deal easier than trying to guess where you are going. The explanations and examples are simple to understand and will make the course fun when you do take it. The example problems and solutions will familiarize the student with what he will see in the subject.

Second, this book unites the parents with the student. That is, it enables a parent to have the ability to help the student even

---

[1] Zuckerman, Mortimer B. *Why Math and Science Education Means More Jobs.* "U.S. News Weekly" Sep 27, 2011

though as a parent they may have absolutely no math and science skills or knowledge. It is written in a manner such that parents with no previous exposure to these subjects can learn right along with their child. **This book is designed to help parents help their child to become better in life than they were, to achieve more and have a better standard of living.** It should be every parents wish and desire to see that their children do better in life than they did. Math and science teachers in high school are in many cases inadequate, especially in motivating and properly explaining the subject to students taking math and science. Parents can make a huge difference. Parents that are already home schooling their children prior to having them enter high school will find this book the "home schooler's friend.

Parents have to be involved to some degree. When I went to school, school hours were from 8:00 to 3:30. Teachers had more time with students. Now time is compressed such that teachers have to race to get the material across. Thus parents have to pave the way so that students can maximize their exposure to these teachers.

There is actually a third objective in this book to aid the two main purposes. There is a strategic technique to gaining the most of what the teachers are trying to teach in math and physics. With a few tricks and techniques that will be explained in this book, a student can learn twice as much in half the expended time. This will be covered further in the book.

Nowhere is this desire for their children to succeed more pronounced than in immigrants that come to this country. Every parent should have this same drive for their children to achieve more than they did. If you are in the lower economic spectrum, then you know that you don't want this same position for your children. This is your opportunity to make your children's future better and to improve the job market and competitive position of our country.

If you think that you just don't know anything about these subjects and therefore can't help your child, then this book is for you. If you are knowledgeable or if you are not knowledgeable in these subjects, this book gives you a tool to help your child prepare for high school. The purpose of this book is to take the fear of these subjects from the parent(s) so that they can be effective in helping their child. For the child it explains clearly what the course is about without making him become overwhelmed. The explanations are clear and the examples are simple to understand. The course problems presented are representative of the material and will orient the student for the course. When the student goes to class he will be prepared.

The purpose of this book isn't necessarily to try to get every child into a 4 year college. Science and math are in desperate need for technicians and industrial workers that don't require a four year degree, but do require math and science skills. There are jobs right now available that pay extremely well that are going unfilled because there are not enough high school graduates with these skills. I know this from articles in the news and from first-hand experience working on the work force development committee and education subcommittee in Alabama's "Manufacture Alabama" program.

There are many two year programs in schools that can't fill their quotas of students because high school students graduating today do not have the skills for these spots. Worse there are students graduating that could have filled these jobs, but didn't know how to take advantage of their time in school to be prepared for them. Worse their parent could have spent the time, if they only knew how, to help their child. The purpose of this book is get to the student and parent before starting these courses so that he or she will do well and have a better opportunity for himself (herself) and a better opportunity for our country to meet the challenges of the future.

Introductory Overview

I didn't give it much thought when I was growing up, I just leaned toward math, physics, and chemistry. I liked these subjects and did well. I wasn't a great student in so far as I was more interested in running cross country, playing intermural sports and "hanging" with my buddies. In fact, I was just a normal high school kid.

However, when I entered the 9th grade, I decided to listen and work hard right from the start in algebra. I had heard it was hard. I had also learned in math prior to 9th grade that you had to really concentrate during class. I had also learned that if you didn't catch on in the beginning it was almost impossible to catch up. So, instead of goofing off and socializing like I did in Latin and History in the 9th grade, I paid attention in algebra. I also had learned to speak up and ask questions if I didn't understand something. In the 9th grade, I decided to be ruthless and press the teacher until I totally understood what he was saying. I also learned that I did better if I sat up front. Some classes you could find your own seat and some the teacher had a specific roll call.

At any rate I did well in all my math courses, always getting B's for a grade. I did not take chemistry in high school, but did take physics in my senior year and obtained my one A for the year. It was a nice way to end my high school career. I also obtained an award in the school science fair for my physics project. My physics teacher, Mr. Patrick was an outstanding teacher and a good guy. He, at my request, loaned me a chemistry book for the summer. I worked the entire summer to make money for college and didn't really look at the book much.

I don't know how it happened, but I ended up majoring in chemistry in college. I was so worried my freshman year of college that my not having taken the course in high school would put me at a distinct disadvantage. However, I managed a B in the freshman chemistry course and loved the subject so well I majored in it and minored in math and physics. I even took advanced organic chemical preparations in college and landed a B in this subject. Organic chemistry was one of the toughest courses in college.

Now you might say I had an aptitude for math and you might be correct. However, I did have to work at it to do well. I learned techniques that helped me throughout my math and science years and will share these in this book.. I think it is more how you take the course than aptitude. My daughter took math in high school and did not like it and did not have, in my opinion, an aptitude for the subject. I worked with her and she obtained A's in high school math, even calculus.

She did not take any math after high school. She majored in Journalism in college, worked in her field, then went back to get a Master in Divinity, and is currently writing her doctoral dissertation in Religion while teaching at a fine University. The point is, she did well, but she had help and encouragement from parents. It is my contention that every student needs help and guidance from a parent that cares. You just can't rely on teachers because some teachers are just not very good. I was lucky and had great high school teachers in both math and physics.

I remember having a high school English teacher in the 11th grade who was horrible. I did poorly. In addition to his being incompetent, he and I had a personality clash as well. He grudgingly gave me a C in the course, only because I got an 86 in the New York State Regents exam that we were all required to take at the end of the course. I had had D's in the course during the year. I had B's in my other years in English. I had an outstanding 8th grade English teacher, Mrs. Sullivan who gave me a great foundation that carried me through high school and enabled me to overcome a terrible 11th grade teacher. However, to be honest, if I had listened to this terrible teacher and didn't tune him out because he was so bad, I might have gotten a B in this subject anyway.

Even if you don't have an aptitude or think you know anything at all about these subjects, you can still help your child to succeed. This book will put forth enough material in simple form to take away the excuse that you are inadequate to help your child. You are not "math stupid" even if you think you are and have never done well in the subject. We will cover each of the subjects in the order they are given in high school. Algebra is first, then geometry, then chemistry, trigonometry, physics, and calculus. There are only 6 subjects. Two of these, trigonometry and calculus, are optional. So there are only 4 subjects to truly worry with. These 4 subjects can make the difference between success in life and failure. Wow, think of it, four subjects can affect your child's entire life.

It is also just possible that helping your child may also help you in your life as well. Even if it doesn't help you with your career, it will give you the wonderful satisfaction that you did something with your life by helping someone succeed. There is no better feeling than helping someone. There is no better feeling than watching that someone succeed.

And it isn't just helping that son or daughter succeed, but it is helping your country succeed in an ever competing global community of countries. We used to be the country to envy with regards to technology and science breakthroughs. But other countries have surpassed us as evidenced by tests given to students in 65 countries every three years since the year 2000.

Every 3 years starting in the year 2000 an international testing program for countries was established and coordinated by the Organization for Economic Cooperation and Development (OECD). The testing program is for high school students as they end their high school years. Most of the countries (65 in all) in the world participate. The study is conducted by The Program for International Student Assessment (PISA).

The latest PISA study was conducted in 2012. The study measures student's knowledge and ability in reading, math, and science literacy. In the 2012 study the results which have just now come out showed the United States doing poorly compared to other countries. More and more countries have been surpassing us since the testing began in 2000.

CHAPTER 1 (For Parents and Grandparents)

This book is for the parent (grandparent) who wants his child to succeed and have a better life. I am including grandparents in this section such that when parents are mentioned, this also includes grandparents. With two parent breadwinners in most families these days, it sometimes falls to grandparents to pick up the slack from the traditional single bread winner family of the 1950's and 1960's.

All of us should want our children to do better than we did. My grandparents came to this country so that they could provide a better life for their children and their children's children. My paternal grandfather came from Italy around 1900. He came to this country with his young wife and his brother. He was a brick mason and he and his brother spent their life putting up buildings in New York City. They would go to work each day, lay massive amounts of bricks and return home for dinner at 6:00 P.M. They managed to raise three children (two girls and one boy). The boy was my father.

My father made it through high school and became a salesman for an oil company. He called on apartment buildings in the Bronx and sold them on converting from coal heat to oil heat. He did well and when I was 10, my parents and my brother and I moved from a one bedroom apartment in the Bronx to a two bedroom home just across the Bronx line in Westchester, New York.

My maternal grandfather also from Italy was a plasterer. He spent his life putting up plaster walls and later attaching plaster figurines to churches. He met my grandmother, who also had come over from Italy with her family and they married and had three children. Two boys and one girl. The girl was my mother.

My grandmother was entrepreneurial. Later in life, my grandfather managed to build a house on a piece of land in Ardsley, New York. He was a good carpenter as well as plasterer. They had about one acre of land that bordered on two acres of county property that later was used for the Sprain Brook Parkway.

My grandmother started planting strawberries and sold these on the side of the road at a small stand that my grandfather built for her. They grew their planting from a small patch to at least an acre over time. This gave them added income and helped them in later life.

My parents partially helped me financially get through college. I was lucky that I had managed to land many jobs going through school. One of which was as a waiter for a combination country club/night club in Westchester. At any rate, I was the first to graduate from college on both sides of the family. I majored in chemistry and minored in math and physics in college. I worked as an industrial chemist for many years holding jobs as laboratory superintendent, process and quality control engineer and chemical plant manager. During my career I went back to school at night and obtained an MBA. In my later career I went into sales and marketing and held many positions in both sales engineering and sales management.

My daughter is currently writing her dissertation for her PhD in Religion while she is teaching at a fine University. My grandparents dream and hope for their children and their children's children to do better than they did was strong and powerful. I am writing this book to help those parents who want the same for their children and their children's children. Let me tell you, it just doesn't happen; parent (s) have to have the dream and make it come true. You cannot expect any school to make it happen for you. It just doesn't work that way. You can't brow beat your child, you must encourage them and show them you care. Working with them on preparing for each high school course shows them you care and that it is most important. They will get the message a whole lot better if you work with them than if you try to force them. This book will help you work with them.

So as a parent what do you do. Well, having purchased this book is a good first step. The second step is to congratulate yourself for taking the first step because taking the first step means that you are going to take an active role in your child's future. Taking an active role is the key to your child's success. Understand that you do not have to know a thing about these subjects. You may have even failed them or just squeaked through them or in many cases didn't even take some of these courses.

This book is to give you as well as your child an understanding of these subjects without a major effort. Having knowledge of the subject before taking it, is a real advantage that cannot be over emphasized. A little bit of exposure before taking the class will make all the difference in the world. As a parent, learning about the subject from this book will take away the fear that you yourself may have had all your life about these subjects. Taking away your fear will also lessen your child's fear. Fear of these subjects can make it harder to learn. A little fear is good in that it might motivate, but too much fear is a negative motivator. Don't expect for you and your child to understand everything. Learn what you can. There is no test. Just having looked at and worked with the material and problems will help your child.

This book is designed to make you as the parent comfortable with the purpose and overview of the subject. You don't have to be an expert in these subjects. You just have to know what they are about to encourage your child. Having a basic understanding of a subject will make you feel more comfortable discussing it with your child. You don't have to have a rocket science mentality to understand the basics and purpose of the math and science subjects. This book takes each subject and does the following:

1. Provides a simple easy to understand overview of what the subject is about.
2. Provides a short discussion of the uses of the subject so that as a parent you can explain why it is important.
3. Provides a 1 page method for teaching your child how to get the best grade for his efforts. It is a guide to taking the course starting on day one in class, which gives your child a procedure that he can use that will absolutely guarantee success. If he follows this guide he will be a winner. Recommend that he only do 3-5 pages a day depending on the subject. Start with 3 per day.
4. It provides examples that clearly demonstrate what your child will see during the course so it will not seem foreign to him or her.
5. It takes the fear and mystery out of these subjects for both the parent and the child. There is nothing more debilitating than fear of the subject. Knowing what it is about and how to take the course will take away the demotivating fear for the student. As a parent, feeling comfortable about the subject will make you more effective in encouraging your child.
6. It provides practice problems and solutions that give you and your child the essence of the subject. As a parent, it would be good to look at these before or together with

your child. It is also a great way of bonding with him or her to do these together. Don't worry if some of it does seem difficult because much of it will register and help your child later in class.

This book starts with algebra and then proceeds to other subjects as they would be given in a normal high school rotation. Geometry is next, then chemistry, physics, and finally trigonometry and calculus (optional in most schools) for those who decide to really go further with a scientific endeavor.

This book provides just the right amount of subject so that it isn't overwhelming. No one is going to take a 400 page book on algebra and study it on their own. However, a small amount of the subject at a strategic point can make the difference between solid success and failure.

CHAPTER 2 (For Students)

Okay, you have this book in front of you now. Maybe your parents or grandparents forced it on you or maybe you are so enlightened that you went out and obtained this book on your own. It doesn't matter how you got here. What matters is where you go next with it.

If I told you that a little effort now in reading this book on the subject that you are getting ready to take will make it easier and use less of your time; and if the time you spend reading this book on the subject will get you an A would you consider reading further? If I also told you that this book can make the difference from working at McDonalds to starting off out of high school with a path towards a fine paying job would you consider reading further; a job where you can get a great car, a boat, and make a nice life with your significant other?

If you think you absolutely have to go to college to get this life, you would be wrong. College would certainly be great, but you can still have it all without college if you are good in math and science in school. I belonged to a state industrial group that had as its main problem obtaining high school graduates that were functional in math and science.

Going to college would be best, but second best would be going into industry with a high paying job. If you want to get to college, this book can get you there as well. The job market in the sciences and engineering for college graduates has always been strong. No matter which way you go (college or not) this book will make a difference in your life. It can make the difference between a low college entrance score and a scholarship score. Or, if you don't go to college, it can make the difference between working a fast food job to making a significant career in industry right out of high school.

Oh yeah, this book can do that if you take a small amount of time to read it. Don't try to read it all in one sitting because that would be next to impossible. You would be scared to death and probably give up and put the book somewhere and never look at it again. Do a few minutes each day. Working on 3 pages per day won't kill you. If you find that it comes easy for you then up it to 5, but that is a lot to absorb. Don't worry if you don't understand it right away. It is designed to give you a feel for the subject so it will be easier when you take it. Some of the material will be difficult for you and some will seem relatively easy. Also, make sure you read the part in each subject on how to take the subject to maximize your results from the time you spend.

If you are bent on going to college, this book can get you there. And, if you want to go to college and have a real degree in a science or an engineering field this book can get you there. Let's face it, what this country needs is more productive people in the sciences and math. There has been a recent study that has shown the more math, science, and engineers graduating, the more jobs that will be created.

You may root for Alabama, Ohio State, LSU, or Penn State. You likely have a team that you admire and follow. If your team was doing poorly and you could help them, I know you would. Well right now our home team, the United States is sucking wind in the race against other countries in math and science. Out of 65 countries we ranked 36th in math and 28th in Science. So, 35 countries beat us in math and 27 in science. We are below average in the testing scores in these subjects. Countries like Viet Nam, Ireland, and Poland beat us. That is no way to remain competitive in the world. Our American team needs you.

It is well known that improved math and science education increases jobs overall. So read this and be prepared for your next course whether its algebra, geometry or chemistry. It's not too late. Your home team needs you. It's the right thing to do for you, your significant other, your future children, and your country. Read on and I will show you all the tricks to making it happen as well as providing you with the understanding so you can hit the ground running on your first day of class. I will take the mystery out of these courses so the material will not seem overwhelming and impossible. It may seem that way as you read this, but it will clear up the more you are exposed to it.

For those of you who like things clear and black and white without any bull, math and science are for you. Two times two is always going to be 4. There is no politics or mumbo jumbo in the world of math and science. The laws of science and math are real and they are consistent.

This book hits the highlights of the course so that you the student are on the right track from the first day, thus enabling you to focus properly. You won't be bouncing off walls trying to get a foothold. You will already have a foothold. You won't come home and be hitting your head against a stone wall of despair trying to figure out what to do. You will know and go right to it. Let's get started.

CHAPTER 3 ALGEBRA

FIRST: If you haven't already done so, go back and read the section on "The purpose of this book" and "The Introductory Overview" before you start. Most important, if you are a student, go back and read Chapter 2 " For Students". It's only 2 pages.

So what is algebra really?

In a nutshell, it is finding an unknown quantity. Algebra is divided into two halves as follows:

1. Solving an equation already in existence.

2. Making an equation that will provide an answer to a problem.

Okay, so what is an equation?

An equation is a mathematical equality. Oh, so what does that mean? Well it means that everything on one side of an equal sign (=) is the same value as everything on the other side of the (=) sign. **Think of an equal sign as a seesaw that is totally horizontal and must remain horizontal.**

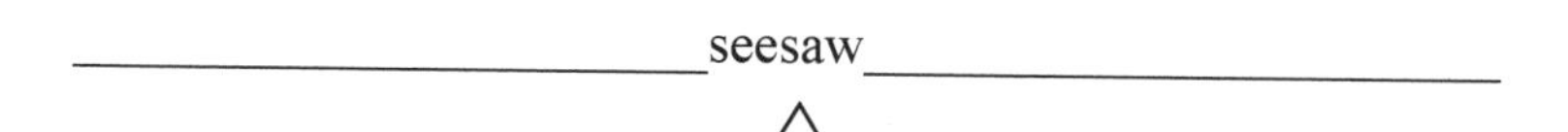

The rule is that the seesaw must always be horizontal. Everything on the right side must be the same weight as everything on the left side. Pretend that the weight on the right and the weight on the left are equal distance from the center so that the effect of distance does not matter. So if you add a 150 pound person on the left, you must add something of equal weight on the right.

You could put a 150 pound person on the left and two 75 people on the right. Or instead of two 75 pound people, you could put one 75 pound person and three 25 pound sacks of cement to balance the 150 pound man on the left.

Let's look at it this way:

75 lb. man
150 lb.man _________________________________ 3 sacks/pot.
^

The 75 pound man is holding the three 25 pound sacks of potatoes in his lap. This is to keep the seesaw level (horizontal).

Now let's convert the seesaw to an equal sign and turn it into an equation as follows;

150 pound man= 75 pound man + 3 sacks of potatoes

Where each sack of potatoes weighs 25 pounds.

Let's call S equal to one 25 pound sack of potatoes. So S= 25pounds.
Let's just use the actual weights of the men without saying they are men as follows:

$$150=75 + 3S$$

We now have an algebraic equation. Remember we said that the first half of algebra was to solve an equation already in existence. So if we did not know the weight of S we would have to solve for S. We already know it is 25, but let's pretend we don't know and solve it using algebra.

We could have used X instead of S. Algebra books love X's. We could have said "Let's call X equal to one 25 pound sack of potatoes." It doesn't matter what letter is used to represent the unknown. For now let's stick with our S. I just wanted to let you know that you could get an equation to solve with any letter. The letter just means it is an unknown.

Okay so going back to our equation:

$$150=75 + 3S$$

Again think of the equal sign as a seesaw where each side must have the same weight. Whatever you do to one side, you must do the same to the other side.

Since it is easier to always have the unknown on the left side, let's get the unknown to the left.

To do that we simply turn the equation around. Turning the equation around still keeps it in balance just like turning a seesaw around. So,

$$75 + 3S = 150$$

Again if this were a seesaw the man would have the 3 sacks of potatoes on his lap. We could change this by putting the three sacks of potatoes below the man so that he is sitting on the potato sacks instead of them sitting on his lap. He would probably be more comfortable. It is the same with the equation. We can move the 3S and 75 without disturbing the equation as follows:

$$3S + 75 = 150$$

Nothing has really changed, but now it is easier to work with.

Let's continue by stating –**Whatever you do to one side, you have to do to the other side. This is algebra.**

The whole half of the equation solving portion of algebra uses this principle. The course teaches you the tricks to solve the equation by making equal changes to both sides.

Let's demonstrate how this works in simple steps.

First, let's subtract 75 from both sides so we can deal better with S.

Subtracting 75 from both sides gives us:

$$3S = 75$$

Okay for those of you still thinking about the seesaw, you are probably wondering how we subtracted half the weight of the man. We could cut him in half (yuck) or think of him as two 75 pound men, one sitting on the other's lap (uncomfortable). Okay, at any rate you get the idea that the equal sign must always have the same quantities on both sides.

So now to continue to solve for S.

What do you do to both sides to get S all by itself so we know what value it is?

Right, you guessed it. We divide both sides by 3 as follows:

$$3S/3 = 75/3$$

or

$$S = 25$$

We're not done with the seesaw yet. We have now convinced you that you can do the same thing to both sides of the seesaw and it remains level. Now let's talk about one side of the seesaw. It doesn't matter which side, but let's say the right side. As long as you do the same thing to the top of the side that you do to the bottom, the seesaw remains level.

For example, if two people come up to the seesaw at one end and one puts his hands down on the top of the seesaw and the other lays down underneath and puts his on the seesaw directly below the man's hands so that only the wood of the seesaw is between their hands. If they both exert the same force on the seesaw, it won't budge. Now if they both doubled their force it still won't budge. It remains horizontal.

It is the exact same thing with an equation. You can multiply the entire equation or any individual part of the equation by say 1/1 or 2/2 or 4/4 or A/A because all these are going to keep the equation of the same value or balance just as we did with the seesaw. If you can grasp this simple analogy you are halfway to an A.

That's it. You now know the first half of algebra—solving equations. Sure there will be more complicated equations as you go. We will present a few of these to show what you can expect and to show some techniques that will help you. Just remember what you do to one side, you must do to the other. And you can do things to the right or left side as long as that thing keeps it in balance like multiplying top and bottom of a number by 1 in the form of 2/2 or (same whatever)/(same whatever). It's really just a game. Think of it that way and it could actually be fun.

Now, let's talk about how you can get an A in the course with not a great deal of effort or at least not as much as you thought. It's all in listening, timing, and practice. Just like any game or sport. Only this game will make the difference in your life. It's going to separate the successful people in life from the not successful. The ones who get the love of their life, have the nice house, boat and kids, and can retire early. And you can still be cool. You can be a nerd in Algebra and still be cool.

First rule. Sit up front, if at all possible. When I sat up front, I aced the course I was taking. In the back I didn't. I could come up with reasons like you won't be looking at that sexy somebody in front of you and having thoughts about them. Reasons don't matter. Get up front or as close to front as possible and focus on what the teacher says (no matter how bad he or she is).

Algebra is not a subject you can learn easily from a book. You can read history books and learn, but it is almost impossible to pick up an algebra book and learn. That's the hard way. You need to truly listen in class and use the text book for reinforcement and practice problems. AND YOU HAVE TO DO THAT FROM THE VERY BEGINNING BECAUSE ALGEBRA BUILDS ON EACH THING YOU LEARN.

And when you don't understand something, don't be a wimp and let it go. Have an attitude. Ask the teacher. Make your teacher earn his or her pay[2] and answer the question until you understand.

Now I am going to tell you how I became a whiz in math. It wasn't intelligence, it was a trick. First, I learned somewhere about retention time. You forget half of what you learned in the first hour after class and it goes downhill each hour from then. So how do you keep what you learned in your brain?

---

[2] Please be aware that teachers are vastly underpaid and that my comment was in no way disrespectful to the profession of teaching. Teaching is one of the most personally rewarding professions and one of the most important for the future of our world. Most teachers are teaching because they want to make a difference.

Method and technique to make an A in Algebra:

1. Get a notebook that is bound. One that you will not lose the pages.
2. Take notes on one side of the page, leaving the other blank. You can write your notes on the right side or the left depending on which is easier for you. I always used the left side.
3. Purchase a good red marking pen.
4. As quickly after class as possible fix your illegible notes. I used to stay in the seat for 5 minutes before running to the next class. I would use my red pen to mark my notes so I could decipher them later on. When you are hurrying to take notes sometimes what seems clear when you are writing cannot be understood when you get home. But it is most likely still fresh in your mind right after class so you can write over in red a less than clear symbol or word that you wrote to make it clear for later.
5. Before you start any other homework copy your notes from one side of the page to the other. This reinforces what you have learned in class and makes it much neater. By having both pages side by side you can always refer to the original if you copied wrong. I always gave myself a treat when I started doing the copying. When I sat down to do algebra I had a coke and a candy bar. It was my special time. Now a coke and a candy bar would give me heartburn, but I was younger then.
6. After you have copied your notes, then do your algebra homework problems. **DO THEM ALL.** Don't be lulled into false security because they seem redundant. Some may be redundant and some may have just a slight trick to them that you would not have caught if you skipped the problem. Without question the problem you skipped will show up on an exam in some form.
7. Check your answers. If you got it wrong, fix it and highlight it in yellow. If you can't figure it out and have struggled with it, then the next day in class the light will shine when your teacher goes over it. But do your best to struggle if necessary to figure it out.
8. Highlight the problems that you missed.

9. Redo the highlighted problems that you missed first time.
10. Write down in red on the problem itself any questions you might have so you can ask them in class.
11. Now you are ready for class.
12. The teacher will likely go over homework and then present new material. If you have done everything above, you will find that it is just refreshing to go over the homework problems that you have already done.
13. Don't get cocky.
14. When you study for your test do practice problems from your homework, especially the ones that were highlighted in yellow. If you miss one, mark it in some way and do it again before the test. Make sure you read over your notes from class before the test.
15. This next item can very well make the difference between a B and an A. Many teachers will give students their test back. So if you can find someone from the previous year who still has their tests, get their test and make sure you can do every problem on it. The teacher will not give the same test to you, but knowing how to do the previous year's test is a great way to help know what the teacher considers important. It is a great learning tool. Don't shirk on this one. Find someone who has taken these tests.
16. Smile when your paper comes back with a nice high mark. Because if you follow the above this is what is going to happen.
17. When you do well be prepared for your friends and peers to give you a hard time. Just tell them you find Algebra fun just like a video game. That should shut them up. Don't let them discourage you or make you feel bad for doing well. Just know that they are jealous and would never admit it. Ten years from now when you have the nice home, the great car and boat, and the great significant other, what they think now will be totally insignificant and meaningless.
18. One last thing–Don't miss one class. You can catch up in history or English, but algebra is tough. It's probably 10 times harder than history. If you have to be out sick, try to come in for the algebra class and then go back home. Your parents can write you a note. If you are in

sports, try to fix your schedule to take algebra in the morning so that you are not pulled out at the end of the day for a game or game practice. Some schools like to have special programs where a student leaves class for something. Don't get talked into skipping out on algebra.

Note: When doing homework, some may find that it works better to do it in pieces. Do some now, then take a break, and then come back to it. This is especially true if you hit a wall and can't figure it out. And you will hit walls. Everyone does. It's like going from one level to the next in a video game. When you do hit a wall, take a deep breath and try again or go onto the next problem and then come back to this tough one later. Taking a walk around the block is a great break. Or shooting a couple of hoops. Even doing a couple of pushups is good because it puts oxygen in your brain. Whatever works for you is best. The physical activity is good because it negates the coke and candy bar potential weight gain.

Five Problems with Solutions:

Note any letter footnotes to the upper right of an item. Read these for clarity.

Problem 1:

$$2(7-X) = X + 5$$

Solution:

Do the multiplication first

$$14-2X = X + 5$$

Get all the X's on the left side by subtracting X from both sides

$$14 - 2X - X = 5$$

Here's an interesting thing to use from now on. *When moving a number or letter from one side to the other just change the sign when it is moved. If it's a plus on the right, it becomes a minus on the left.*

Now let's move all the numbers to the right side. Here we would be subtracting 14 from both sides. But remember we said we could just change the sign. In this case a + 14 becomes a – 14 when moved

$$-2X - X = 5 - 14$$[3]

Now let's clean it up by doing the subtractions

$$-3X = -9$$

We could proceed from here in two ways

First we could just multiply both sides by -1

Remember a minus times a minus is a plus so

$$3X = 9$$

Divide both sides by 3

$$X = 3$$

Or we could have solved the equation first so that

$$-3X = -9$$

Becomes

$$-X = -3$$

And then multiplied both sides by -1

$$X = 3$$[4]

---

[3] -2x – x is really -2x plus –x. When you add two minuses the sign stays the same. Thus -2x – x becomes -3x. If it had been -2x –(-x) this would be -2x + x because minus a minus number equals a plus. Thus -2x – (-x) is equal to –x. Just remember this.

[4] Or for those really astute, we could have divided both sides by -3. Remember a minus number divided by a minus number is equal to a plus number same as multiplying. So in this case – 3X divided by – 3 becomes just X. We don't have to write the X as +X because X by itself

Now let's talk about checking your work

Go Back to the original formula now that we know the answer is 3

$$2(7-X) = X + 5$$

So now let's plug in 3 for X

$$2(7-3) = 3 + 5$$

$$2(4) = 8$$

$$8 = 8$$

And so it checks and you know you did it right.

Are you having fun yet?

Problem 2:

Let's do one a little easier and more basic:

$$4X = 2 + 3X$$

Solution:

Moving 3X to the left and changing the sign

$$4X - 3X = 2$$

See by changing the sign we really just subtracted 3X from both sides

$$X = 2$$

Problem 3:

---

means +X. Then we have to divide the other side by -3 which give us -9 divided by -3 equals 3. So we get X = 3.

Remember those fractions you hated. Here they are again.

$$X/2 - 3 = 2 - 2X$$

Solution:

Okay so they want you to solve for X obviously

One simple way to start is to multiply both sides by 2

$$2\,(X/2 - 3) = 2(2-2X)$$

Doing the multiplication

$$X - 6 = 4 - 4X$$

Remember in fractions 2 times ½ = 1 because the 2's cancel out

Okay continuing on let's get the X's to the left

$$X - 6 + 4X = 4$$

And get all the numbers to the right

$$X + 4X = 4 + 6$$

Or simplified

$$5X = 10$$

And then

$$X = 2$$

Okay now let's do the check

$$2(X/2 - 3) = 2(2-2X)$$

Plugging in the 2 for the X

$$2(2/2 - 3) = 2(2-2(2))$$

Remember you do the multiplication and division first so

2(1-3) = 2(2-4)

Now we could proceed two ways from here

We could do the work inside the parenthesis first like this

2(2) = 2(2) or obviously 4 = 4

Or we could have done it this way by multiplying from outside the parenthesis first as follows:

2-6 = 4-8 or -4 = -4

Remember -4 = -4 is really 4 =4
because you can multiply both sides by -1

Anyway it checks either way

As a rule you do everything in the parenthesis first. You can do the multiplication and division and then the addition and subtraction inside the parenthesis before doing the rest of the multiplication and division and addition and subtraction to the rest of the equation. Don't worry if it sounds a little confusing because you will be seeing this again and it will make sense the more you see it and more you work with it. This is just to get you an overview so you won't get Algebra shock when you take the course.

Let's talk Fractions:

Let's do a scary problem.

Scary Problem:

$$\frac{1/2 + 1/3}{1/6}$$

Remember we said we could multiply top and bottom by the same number. So we can multiply by 1/1 or 2/2 or 4/4, etc.

Okay so multiply top and bottom by 6

$$\frac{6}{6}\ \frac{1/2 + 1/3}{1/6}$$

$$\frac{6\,(1/2) + 6(1/3)}{6/6}$$

$$\frac{3 + 2}{1}$$

$$= 5$$

Think of it this way. Supposing you wanted to know how many ½'s were in 5. This would be written 5/(1/2) or five divided by one half.

$$\frac{5}{½}$$

$$5 \text{ x } 2/1 = 10$$

Now think of it in terms of a five dollar bill. If someone asked you how many half dollars were in a 5 dollar bill, you would know that there were ten without much conscious thought.

Okay, you don't have to think this out every time you see a fraction, just remember when you divide by a fraction you invert it and multiply. An inverted fraction is called a reciprocal in math. So all you had to do was multiply by 6/1 in the scary problem. If it had been division by 2/3, then you would have multiplied by 3/2. I hope this takes away the fear of fractions some.

So what's the point of all this equation stuff?

Glad you asked. It may seem like a boring waste of time, but it really is going to help you significantly in life. So you want a practical example. Okay, let's suppose that you are going to go visit a relative who lives 1200 miles from you. Let's suppose that you don't have MapQuest or GPS and you need to know how long it is going to take to drive there.

You look on a map and see that there are three equal segments. The first segment is interstate and you can go 75 mph. The second segment is a state highway and you can go 60 mph. The third is a county road that you can only go 45 mph.

To solve this problem, let T = the total time to get there.

Then you could say that:

One third the total time (T) you would be going 75
One third the total time (T) you would be going 60
One third the total time (T) you would be going 45

1/3 T (75) + 1/3 T (60) + 1/3 T (45) = 1200

Doing the math it becomes:

25 T + 20 T + 15 T = 1200

60 T = 1200

T = 20 hours

You can then decide how much time you would have to add for stopping for gas and food. You would then be able to decide whether you want to drive straight through with a buddy sharing the drive or take two days for the trip.

Let's make it a little more difficult and say that the map really has different segments and speeds as follows:

You look on a map and see that you can slice the route into pieces. You notice ½ of the distance is an interstate that you can go 80 mph. Let's suppose that 1/6 is state highway and you can go 60 mph. You have the last 2/6 or 1/3[5] on a county road in

[5] As a reminder you can multiply the top and bottom of a fraction by the same number and the fraction remains the same. Thus in this case if you multiply the 1/3 by two on top and bottom, you get 2/6. If you add 1/6 and 2/6 you get 3/6, which is ½. Thus ½ plus ½ equals the entire line segment or distance. In the previous problem above, 1/3 + 1/3 + 1/3 equaled the entire line segment or distance.

which you can go 45 mph. You don't believe there are any lights on the county road so that is not an issue.

To solve this problem, let T= the total time to get there.

Then you could say that:

Half the total time you would be going 80
One sixth of the total time you would be going 60
And one third you would be going 45

$\frac{1}{2}T(80) + \frac{1}{6}T(60) + \frac{1}{3}T(45) = 1200$

$40T + 10T + 15T = 1200$

$65T = 1200$

$T = 18.46$ hours

.46 hours is equal to .46 times 60 minutes in an hour. So .46 times 60 is equal to 27.6 minutes or you could round it to 28 minutes. So this trip would take 18 hours and 28 minutes.

This may look difficult to you, but after taking algebra this is going to be second nature.

The point was to show you that there is practical use of algebra as well as work use.

You will be learning many helpful equations or formulas in both algebra and geometry. It should also be pointed out that these subjects truly teach your brain to analyze and figure things out. This exercising of your brain is the same as exercising a muscle in your body. The more exercise the stronger your muscle. A strong brain means more success in your endeavors in life.

Last night my wife asked me for help while she was making a bolster pillow. A bolster pillow is a tubular pillow that you see on a sofa or at the head of a bed for decoration. She needed to know how much material she needed to go around in a circle around a diameter of 10 inches.

I remembered from geometry that the circumference of a circle was given by the formula—πd. The symbol π is Greek and pronounced pie just like apple pie. Π is simply a ratio of circumference to diameter and is equal to 3.14. For every inch in diameter, there is 3.14 inches in circumference going around the circle. (The circumference is the circle around a point.) Thus I was able to tell my wife that she needed ten times 3.14 or 31.4 inches of yarn to go around the 10 inch diameter. She rounded off and cut 31 and a half inches and it was just fine.

Don't let this scare you. Have faith that in a year's time using my method will enable you to get it. You have to get it because you will see questions like this on tests for jobs in industry and on tests for college entrance. Plus I want you to get an A and be able to whip up on those other countries that have pulled ahead of us.

To continue on with the reasons for learning Algebra, let's list a few as follows:

1. Better paying career job out of high school.
2. For those going to college, it will provide opportunity for serious scholarship money. See the attached article from my local Birmingham paper about scholarships. The attached news article shows the amount for grade average and ACT scores (college entrance tests). For an ACT of 30 and a score of B+ in high school, the scholarship pays $ 9,000 per year. Even a B average qualifies. With a B and an ACT of 24 you get $3,500 per year according to the article. You have to be an Alabama resident or live in certain counties in Florida and Mississippi to qualify. Most every state has similar programs for residents of their state.
3. Doing well in Algebra will help you dramatically in Geometry and in the Sciences because they all use Algebra.
4. Doing well in Algebra and then the other math and sciences will open up doors in many fields like medicine (from technicians to doctors), engineering, computer programming, technicians in all fields, technical maintenance of high tech equipment, technical sales, and much more. A programmer will have to know Algebra because he will be called

upon to write programs that include formulas and equations some that he may have to develop.

5. Getting into two year technical schools. Technical schools let students go right into high tech jobs that pay well and are extremely interesting. Industry is crying for these graduates and paying to get them. Many industries will provide tuition assistance to their employees to go to these schools. The key is to do well in science and math. Algebra is the first step.
6. Algebra will improve the math skills that you missed in earlier grades. You will learn many of the things you had trouble with in the past. Just keep a red pen to mark those things that you have forgotten as you come to them in Algebra. Call them rules and memorize them. One of the best ways to memorize is to practice these rules with the problems given to you for homework.

High-Quality Academic Programs and Great Scholarships for Birmingham Area Students!

NEW!

The University of South Alabama is pleased to increase academic scholarships for resident and non-resident students through the new

MITCHELL-MOULTON SCHOLARSHIP INITIATIVE

Available for 2014 High School Graduates. Apply today!

These are the scholarships listed from the University of South Alabama for Alabama residents plus Mississippi students from George, Greene, Harrison, Jackson, Perry and Stone Counties and Florida students from Escambia and Santa Rosa counties.

From the University of South Alabama Website April 2014:

ACT Composite Score	SAT Equivalent (SAT Critical Reading + Math)	Minimum High School GPA	Annual Amount	4 Year Total Amount
33 or higher	1440 or higher	3.5	$11,000	$44,000
32	1400-1430	3.5	$9,000	$36,000
30-31	1330-1390	3.5	$8,000	$32,000
28-29	1250-1320	3.5	$5,000	$20,000
24-27	1090-1240	3.0	$3,500	$14,000
23	1050-1080	3.0	$2,500	$10,000

ACT Composite Score	SAT Equivalent (SAT Critical Reading + Math)	Minimum High School GPA	Annual Amount	4 Year Total Amount
33 or higher	1440 or higher	3.5	$12,000	$48,000

32	1400-1430	3.5	$10,000	$40,000
30-31	1330-1390	3.5	$9,000	$36,000
28-29	1250-1320	3.5	$6,500	$26,000
27	1210-1240	3.5	$5,000	$20,000

Problem 4:

This is a real life equation that one of the technicians had trouble with while calibrating a sensing device in a power plant.

$3(2ABX) = 3(XAB + 5AB)$ He needed to know X

Solution:

It looks difficult and maybe impossible, but it's not

First, let's do the multiplication as follows:

$$6\ ABX = 3\ XAB + 15\ AB$$

Remember you can divide each side by the same thing (number or letter)

So let's divide both sides by AB

$$6X = 3X + 15$$
$$6X - 3X = 15$$

$$3X = 15$$

$$X = 5$$

In algebra class they will start you off with easier problems than I am showing you, but you will eventually see problems like these.

Equation 2:

There are one or two equations that you will be given. There are also formulas that will be given to you, like formulas for travel distance;

Distance (D) = Speed (S) x (small x means times)[6] Time (T)

D = S x T

So if you are travelling at 60 mph for 3 hours, then

D = 60 x 3 or 180 miles

We will cover this more in the next pages. For now let's look at an equation, which is the most likely equation to be found on the final exam in any algebra class. It is called the Quadratic Equation and looks like this:

Equation 3: The quadratic equation:

$$x = \frac{-b \pm \sqrt{b^2 - 4ac}}{2a}.$$

The plus-minus symbol "±" indicates that both

$$x = \frac{-b + \sqrt{b^2 - 4ac}}{2a} \quad \text{and} \quad x = \frac{-b - \sqrt{b^2 - 4ac}}{2a}$$

So there will be two answers to this equation because you do the formula once with –b + etc. and once with –b – etc.

Don't let this one scare you, it is really very simple once you know what you are supposed to do.

Let's just do one and you will see what I mean.

Problem 5:

When you see an equation that looks like this:

$2X^2 + 10X + 8 = 0$, then you use the quadratic equation.

---

[6] Some textbooks use little x to denote multiplication and some use a dot and some use an asterisk.

Basically the quadratic equation uses the numbers to solve for X.

The letters a, b, and c in the equation are as follows:

The a is the 2, the b is the 10 and the c is the 8 in the above.

Sometimes you will see it explained this way;

$aX^2 + bX + c = 0$ where a is the amount before the X^2, b is the amount before the X and c is the number by itself.

From here it is just a matter of substitution as follows:

$2X^2 + 10X + 8 = 0$

So a = 2
b = 10
c = 8

$$x = \frac{-b \pm \sqrt{b^2 - 4ac}}{2a}.$$

Using the + in the plus or minus first:

x = -10 + square root of (10^2 – 4 (2x8)
Divided by 2x2

Or doing some math

-10 + square root of 100-64
Divided by 4

Continuing on with the math

-10 + square root of 36
Divided by 4

Which comes out to

-10 + 6
Divided by 4

Or
-4/4 = -1

So X = -1

Doing the same thing for when it is minus in the (plus or minus),

X = -10 – square root of (10^2 – 4 (2x8)
Divided by 2x2

Or doing some math

-10 – square root of 100-64
Divided by 4

Continuing on with the math

-10 – square root of 36
Divided by 4

Which comes out to

-10 – 6
Divided by 4

(This could have been written -10 + (-6). Remember in adding two minuses the sign doesn't change and in this case it is -16. Had it been -10 – (-6) it would have been 4 because a minus a minus is a plus. So – (-6) is really plus 6. You will learn more of this in class and it will be second nature as time goes on).

(-10-6)/4

-16/4 = -4

So X = -4

So X is either -1 or -4 or both

Let's check it out and plug in for each as follows:

Plugging -1 into the equation

$$2X^2 + 10X + 8 = 0$$

$$2(-1^2) + 10(-1) + 8 = 0$$

$$2 - 10 + 8 = 0$$

$$0=0$$

So we know that -1 fits the equation

So now let's try -4

$$2(-4^2) + 10(-4) + 8 = 0$$

$$2(16) - 40 + 8 = 0$$

$$32 - 40 + 8 = 0$$

$$0=0$$

So -4 also works, thus both answers are correct.

Labels for Formulas/problems in Algebra:

You will be given specific formulas that are standard algebraic formulas. By now you are wondering what the difference between a formula and an equation is. Well basically a formula is a specific equation such as the following:

1. D = S x T,

Distance is in miles, Speed is in miles per hour and Time is in hours.

It would be well at this point to introduce the algebra concept of crossing out labels to be sure that the answer and the components making up the answer are using the correct labels.

So S x T would be as follows:

S is in miles per hour represented by miles/hours.
T is in hours represented by hours.

Thus we have S x T as $\frac{\text{miles}}{\text{hour}} \times \frac{\text{hours}}{1}$ = miles because the hour(s) cancel each other out so that D must be in miles. We put hours over 1. You can do this because it is simply hours and not hours per something. It is easier to see by putting the one in.

Let's look at some more formulas:

2. A = LW for area of a rectangle, where L is Length and W is Width and A is area.

   So if the Length is 20 feet and the Width is 10 feet then the area is:

   A = 20 ft. x 10 ft.

   A = 200 square feet.

Notice how the label (ft. becomes squared because it is ft. multiplied by ft.) Remember 2x2 is 2^2. It is the same with the labels, ft. x ft. is ft^2.

Now it is a good check to use these labels. You could have had the length in feet and the width in inches. This would not work. They both have to be in the same label measurement. Otherwise you would have feet inches for the area and this would not make sense.

If you measured 20 feet for the length and 12 inches for the width and multiplied them together, what would the 240 mean. Would it be square feet or square inches. In fact it would be neither. It would be meaningless. You would have to change the 12 inches to feet, which would be 1 foot and the area would be 20 square feet (20 ft. x 1 ft.). Or you could change the 20 feet to inches which would be 240 inches which would make the area (240 inches x 12 inches) 2880 square inches.

3. Changing Centigrade into Fahrenheit.

$$F = 9/5C + 32$$

Let's do one. If it is 100 degrees Centigrade what is the temperature in Fahrenheit?

$$F = 9/5 \times 100 + 32$$

$$F = 180 + 32$$

$$F = 212 \text{ degrees Fahrenheit}$$

These are a few of the formulas that you may see in Algebra. Generally, the formula will be given to you on a test. If you have to memorize a formula the teacher will tell you. You will see this formula on tests in chemistry. There you will have to memorize it. It is on most every final exam and probably on many ACT college entrance exams.

4. Changing Fahrenheit into Centigrade

This is the reverse of the problem in 3 above. The formula for this conversion is

$$C = 5/9(F - 32)$$

Let's now change 212 degrees Fahrenheit into Centigrade.

$$C = 5/9(212 - 32)$$

Do the operation inside the parenthesis first

$$C = 5/9(180)$$

C = 100 degrees Centigrade

5. Area of a circle

$$\underline{A}\text{rea} = \pi r^2$$

Where $\pi = 3.14$
r = radius of a circle

In case you don't know what the radius is, it is the distance from the center of the circle to anywhere on the circles border (circumference). It is also half of the diameter.

Let's do one where the radius is 10 inches.

$$A = 3.14(10)^2$$

$$A = 3.14(100)$$

A = 314 inches

You will be given certain formula equations. You don't necessarily need to know where they came from. Most came from someone taking the time years ago to figure it out. As an example the one above where $C = \pi d$ came from someone measuring the circle lengths for given diameters.

He probably took a nail and put a string on the nail. He measured half of the diameter and then tied it to a pencil and ran it in a circle. He then took a string and laid it on the circle to then straighten it and measure it. The reason he used half the diameter was because once the circle was drawn this way, then the diameter would be twice the length from the nail to the pencil. By doing this he found that the ratio of the circle was always 3.14 times the diameter.

The point is you need to memorize the formulas that you are expected to know and not worry about where they came from so much as how to use them. It may not make sense in the beginning, but at some point it will if you stick with it. It's like driving a car in drivers ed. It would be nice to know how to build an engine, but what you really need is to know how to drive the car. Someday it may be relevant to know how to build an engine. You may be an engineer in an automobile plant and part of your job is to make the engine better. It's the same with algebra formulas. Someday how the formula was developed may be of significance to you.

Even though the automobile was invented over 100 years ago, each year it is made better technologically through the efforts of scientists and engineers. Don't think that everything that is important has already been done. We need good engineers and technical people to make what we have better. Better gas mileage for conserving our atmosphere, better methods to put up satellites, better methods to determine illnesses, and new inventions to provide energy without relying on foreign oil are just a few needs. We have a long way to go and need people with technical backgrounds to make the world a better place.

Six Word Problems and Solutions:

Word problems are the meat of algebra and also the hardest part for students. They are the major part of any college entrance exam in math. They make up a large portion of tests to get jobs in industry and other technical jobs. They will be a major part of technical school work and entrance tests. These are some of the kinds that you will see on tests. Some are relatively easy and some are quite difficult. This is designed to cover the easiest and hardest to give a complete picture of the subject.

Problem 6:

1. Half of a number plus 8 is equal to 15. What is the number.

Solution:

Let X = the number

$\frac{1}{2}X + 8 = 15$

Move the 8 to the right

$\frac{1}{2}X = 7$

Multiply both sides by 2

$X = 14$

Let's check it by substituting 14 into the equation

$\frac{1}{2}(14) + 8 = 15$

$7 + 8 = 15$

Problem 7:

Farmer Brown has a rectangular patch of ground that he wants to plant corn on. He needs to buy seed. The seed package says that the package can plant an area of 30 square feet. He walks down the long side of the patch and finds it measures 20 feet and then he walks down the shorter side and it is 12 feet. How many packages of seed does Farmer Brown need to purchase? Set up an equation and solve the problem.

Solution:

Okay, first we remember the area of a rectangle is

$A = LW$, where

A = Area
L = Length
W = Width

But they want to know how many seed packages are in this area

So we know that one package can handle an area of 30 square feet

Let's let P = the number of packages of Seed
Then P = A/30

So substituting LW for A we get

P = LW/30- this is the equation for the problem

Circle this and label it your equation because part of the word question asked you to set up an equation. Actually setting up the equation is what would be the biggest part of the grade for this question. So to finish the word problem,

P = (20 x 12)/30

P = 240/30

P = 8 packages of seed

Note: Always label your answer. In this case it was packages of seed. It is a good practice because it will make sure you answered the question and some teachers actually take off for failing to label. Sometimes the word question will say 2 points for the equation and 1 for the answer for a total of 3 points for this test question. So make sure you label the equation as your equation for the problem.

Problem 8:

Your brother now works at Best Computers in Chicago. He gets paid a salary plus commission. His salary is \$500 per week plus 5% of everything he sells over \$1,500 dollars. Last week he made \$ 650. How much merchandise did he sell? Show formula used.

Solution:

Let P = his total pay
C = his commission
S = weekly salary
M = total merchandise sales made by your brother in one week

$P = S + C$

$C = .05\ (M-1500)$

$P = S + .05(M-1500)$

Plugging in the numbers

$650 = 500 + .05\ M - 75$

Solving for M

$.05\ M = 225$

M = \$ 4,500 So he sold \$ 4,500 worth of merchandise.

Let's check it

First subtract 1,500 from 4,500

4,500 – 1,500 = \$ 3,000

Then take 5% of 3,000

.05 x 3,000 = \$ 150 Commission

Then his salary plus commission is

\$500 + \$ 150 = \$ 650 so it checks.

Problem 9:

The ratio of two numbers is 7 to one. The sum is 72. What are the two numbers.

Let F = the first number
Let S = the second number

So F/S = 7 and
F + S = 72

Both equations fit the given facts so now we need to solve for S and F

Starting with the first equation (F/S = 7) let's isolate F

Multiply both sides by S

$$F = 7S$$

Now substitute 7S in the second formula for F

$$7S + S = 72$$

$$8S = 72$$

$$S = 9$$

Let's check it:

Substituting 9 for S in the second formula

$$F + 9 = 72$$

$$F = 72-9$$

$$F = 63$$

Now let's double check by plugging both F and S into the ratio formula:

$$F/S = 7$$

Substituting for both

63/9 = 7 to one ration so it is correct. F = 63 and S = 9

Problem 10:

There is 300 miles between Mobile and Birmingham. A freight train leaves Mobile travelling at 60 miles per hour headed to Birmingham. At the same time another freight train leaves Birmingham headed for Mobile travelling at 40 miles per hour. They are on different, but parallel tracks. How long will it take for the two trains to pass each other?

Let's utilize the formula for Distance.

D = S x T

Where D = Distance
S = Speed
T = Time

Let's divide the distance into D and 300-D

One train will travel D and one will travel 300-D when they meet

Let's let the Mobile train have D for its distance
And the Birmingham train have 300-D

Thus the Mobile train formula is D = 60T

And the Birmingham formula is 300-D = 40T

Let's substitute 60T for D

300- 60T = 40 T

100 T = 300

T = 3 hours

So the answer is 3 hours.

Let's check it:

Mobile train $D = 60T$

$D = 60\,(3)$

Mobile distance = 180 miles

Birmingham distance is 120 miles (300-180)

Birmingham train $300\text{-}D = 40T$

$300\text{-}180 = 40T$

$300\text{-}180 = 40(3)$

$120=120$

$120 = 120$ So it checks both ways

We could just as easily have made the Birmingham train equal D. Try it and you still get 3 hours.

Problem 11:

Fred works at an arcade. One of the arcade machines takes quarters for 15 minutes of play and also dimes for 5 minutes of play. The machine records total amount of money and number of coins. When Peter checked it, it read 130 coins and $25.00 total money value. How many quarters are in the arcade machine?

Solution:

So let's set up some formulas of what we know as follows:

$.10\,X + .25\,Y = 25.00$ where X = Dimes and Y = Quarters

We also know that $X + Y = 130$ coins

In the first equation $.1\ X + .25\ Y = 25$, let's multiply both sides by 10

$$X + 2.5\ Y = 250$$

So now our two formulas look like this;

$$X + 2.5Y = 250$$
$$X + Y = 130$$

So if you look at these two, you can see that you can subtract the bottom formula from the top because since they are equal you are subtracting the same amount from both sides. So

$$\begin{array}{r} X + 2.5Y = 250 \\ \underline{X + \quad Y = 130} \\ 1.5Y = 120 \end{array}$$

$$Y = 80 \text{ quarters}$$

Okay, so let's check and see. First X must equal 50 because the total number of coins was 130.

So now let's plug into the formula $.1\ X + .25\ Y = \$\ 25.00$

$$.1\ (50) + .25\ (80) = 25.00$$

$5 + 20 = 25$ and it checks out.

Now these are the kinds of questions that you will see on tests in Algebra on the final exams and on ACT entrance tests. You will have an entire year to work with these kinds of word problems.

Now I want you to go back and take a blank sheet or pad of paper and cover up the solution and answer and try to do each of the problems without looking at the solution. Do them over and over. This is how you truly learn algebra. If you study these over and over, you will be solid when you hit the classroom. If you want to do more, there are plenty of algebra questions on line. Armed with what you have learned in this treatise you can probably do several of these.

Let's just do one more algebra manipulation.

Problem 12:

Solve for x; $(5-15/x)/(x-3) = 2$

Solution:

Let's first get rid of that 15/x by multiplying top and bottom of the left side by x/x. Since $x/x = 1$ we don't have to do anything to the right side.

So multiplying by x/x we get

$$(5x - 15)/ x(x-3) = 2$$

Pulling out the 5 we get

$$5(x-3)/x(x-3) = 2$$

The (x-3) on top and bottom cancel each other out

Leaving

$$5/x = 2$$

Multiplying both sides by x

$$5 = 2x$$

$$x = 5/2 = 2.5$$

Let's check it:

Check:

$$(12.5 -15)/2.5(-.5) = 2$$

$$-2.5/-1.25 = 2$$

Multiply left side by -1/-1

2.5/1.25 = 2

2=2 and it checks.

Summary:

You now have a basic understanding of Algebra. You know what it is going to look like because you have now seen the Reader's Digest version that is the short version of the year- long course. Some of the examples shown to you were on a high level and some on a simple level. School will fill in the spaces between the simple and complex.

With practice this will become second nature. This overview will give you a leg up on doing well in Algebra. The biggest thing is practice, practice, practice. Just like in real estate it is location, location, location. The methods and techniques described in this book will net you an A if followed.

Remember, it's important to know how to use the equations. I have never seen a test in which a student was asked to derive a formula equation. If you go into higher math this may be valuable, but it is not necessary now. Remember, it isn't how to build an engine, it's how to drive the car and knowing the rules of the road.

Also, don't think because you were not good in math in the past that you are going to be poor in Algebra. This is definitely not the case. You could have been mediocre in math in the past and very well become an A student in Algebra. It's a whole new ball game.

Remember, this country needs more of you to go into math and science. It's where the jobs are going to be created. It's where the world can be made a better place and it's where the United States can stand tall amongst the other nations.

Best of luck and success to you,

John D. Forlini

P.S. Here is one last medium-hard optional one for you. If you have gotten this far, you might want to see one more for fun. It's like taking a peak at an upper level in a video game. After this "one last optional one" we will also provide an additional option of 5 more problems and solutions of easy to medium intensity.

Problem 13:

$X^2 + X - 20 = 0$ Solve for X

Solution:

Remember that 0 times 0 is 0.
Actually 0 times anything is 0.

Well if you can get the above equation to two things times each other, then one or both have to be zero.

To get a (-20) by having two numbers multiplied by each other, you could have either (2 x -10) or – 2 x 10 or -4 x 5 or 4 x -5. However, to have a plus X in the middle, it would have to be -4X + 5X because 5X plus -4X is equal to X.

Okay, what in the world am I talking about.

Let's multiply X + 5 times X -4 as follows:

$$
\begin{array}{rl}
X + 5^{7} & \\
\underline{X - 4} & \\
-4X - 20 & \text{This came from -4 times 5} \\
\underline{X^2 + 5X\quad\;\;} & \text{and then X; and X times} \\
X^2 + X - 20 & \text{5 and then times X}
\end{array}
$$

So we are able to factor e $X^2 + X - 20$ into $(X + 5)(X - 4)$

So

[7] Multiplying two algebraic equations is similar to multiplying two numbers like 12 times 14.

$$(X + 5)(X - 4) = 0$$

So then either X+5 or X-4 equals zero or both do.
So then $X + 5 = 0$

$$X = -5$$

And/or

$$X = 4$$

So let's see if either or both fit the original equation.

Let's try -5 first as follows into the original equation;

$$X^2 + X - 20 = 0$$

$$(-5)^2 + (-5) - 20 = 0$$

$$25 + (-5) - 20 = 0$$
$$25 + (-25) = 0$$

Remember -5 times -5 equals plus 25 because a minus times a minus becomes a plus. Also adding two like signs does not change the sign. Thus -5 -20 is -25.

I will let you plug in the 4. Suffice it to say that $X = 4$ is also correct. Obviously, 16 plus 4 minus 20 equals zero. Thus both -5 and 4 fit the equation and the correct answer would be $X = -5$ and $X = 4$.

Believe it or not, by seeing this now, it will definitely sink in when you see it in class. Plus a good teacher will explain this better than I did. A book is only one dimensional learning at best. An audio/video and book together are at best two dimensional. A classroom is 3 dimensional. That is why it is so important to get it right in class. Remember if you don't understand it ask the teacher to explain more. Don't count on asking a friend later. He or she probably knows less than you do. They probably have the same question, but were too timid to ask.

Appendix A (How to Solve Word Problems)

Steps to Solve Word Problems:

1. First and foremost figure out what the problem wants from you. Sounds simple, but half the time this is where we fall down. Are they asking you for speed, numbers of kittens, or time. Whatever it is write it down and then give it a letter. For some reason most people like to use X. However, it is a great practice to use the letter that corresponds to what you are looking for. Go back to the 6 word problems in this book and see what they were asking for again.
2. Write down what units the answer should be in. Is it square feet or degrees Centigrade or number of quarters.
3. Ignore the unnecessary stuff in the word problem. Don't let stuff that is not essential confuse you.
4. If possible draw a picture that is representative of the question. Geometry and Travel questions lend themselves well to pictures.
5. Make a label (letter or number if given) for each item or variable sort of like a table.
   Example would be: Speed = S; Distance = D ; Time = T. If you know what any of these are from the question then instead of Speed = S for instance, write Speed = 50 mph.
6. Set up an equation or equations that satisfy the request and given information. Sometimes just putting the problems words into an equation will give you the guidance to solve the problem. If you are told the Distance is 300 miles and the Speed is 50 mph. Then $300 = 50 \times T$ is one possibility. Translate English terms into algebraic terms. The other half of this appendix lists English terms and what they mean algebraically.
7. Put the equation or equations into its simple easy form. Put all the letters on one side and the numbers on the other. If it's more than one equation, try to manipulate them to look alike. Sometimes this will mean that you don't have all the letters on one side and all the numbers on the right. You will have to play with it.

8. You will always hit that awful problem that you just can't see how to do. Don't waste time on this one, go to the next one. Remember on an ACT entrance exam or other exam most of the time every problem has equal weight. So put this one aside for later. The brain is an amazing entity. Sometimes while you are working on other problems, your brain will be unconsciously working out the solution to the problem you didn't know how to do so that when you go back to it you can solve it.
9. Check your work quickly by substituting your answer back into the original equation. You probably noticed that this is what I did on all the problems shown in this chapter.

Key Words to Look For and their Algebraic Meaning:

1. The English words that denote (+) are sum, add, in addition, more than, and, increased, both, greater than, and plus. An example would be "5 more than X". This would be X + 5.
2. The English words that denote (–) are subtract, less than, decreased by, reduced by, difference, take away, diminished by, and deduct. An example would be "Difference between X and 5". The answer would be X-5. Be careful because "Difference between 5 and X" would be 5-X.
3. The English words that denote (x) are times, times as much, multiply, product, tax on, by, lots of, percent of, and interest on. The tax on goods in Hoover, Alabama is 9%. Tax = .09 x goods.
4. The English words that denote (/) are divided by, divide, quotient, goes into, per, and how many times. An example would be "Maximum five tickets per customer for each show. Show = 5 tickets/customer maximum. Five customers can get how many tickets? 5C x (5/C) or 25 tickets.
5. The English words that denote (=) are equal, is, result, will be, was, gives, yields, sold for, and produced. An example would be "Two scoops of cement mix and 500 pounds of gravel produced a ton of concrete." 2S + 500 = 2,000 pounds. Note: one ton = 2,000 pounds. So 2S =

1,500 and S = 750 pounds of cement mix per scoop. This assumes that the question asked how much each scoop weighed.

Five More Algebra Problems for Fun

Five more algebra problems for fun and learning as follows:

Problem 1:

If a function of x is defined as $f(x) = x^4 + 5$, what is f(2)?

Solution:

First, if you haven't already guessed, f(x) is the same as saying y =

Thus $y = x^4 + 5$ for some value of x. The value that we are asking for is x = 2. Thus f(2) means what is the value of the function $x^4 + 5$ when x = 2.

So it is just a matter of substituting 2 for x in the equation.

$$(2)^4 + 5 = 16 + 5 = 21$$

Two raised to the fourth power is simply (you probably already know this) 2 times 2 times 2 times 2 or 16. Easy way to remember power is to do the square first, which as you know is 2^2. So if 2^2 is 4 then, 2^3 is 8 and one more time would make it 2^4 or 16.

Problem 2:

If $f(x) = -10\ (7)^x + 8$, what is f(3) ?

Solution:

So don't get tricked by the minus sign.

Always do the raising of a power first, thus $7^3 = 343$

Then do the multiplication next

-10 times 343 = -3430

Now do the addition -3430 + 8 = - 3422

Reminder: Pluses and minuses

$4 - 2 = 2$ First grade stuff
$-4 + 2 = -2$ Adding a plus to a minus makes it less minus
$4 - (-2) = 6$ Subtracting a minus number makes it a plus number
$-4 - 2 = -6$ Two minus numbers make it more minus
Note: $-4 - 2$ could also be written $-4 + (-2)$

Problem 3:

If your watch runs one second behind every day and you set it when it was already 15 seconds behind, how many days has it been since you set your watch if it is now 2 minutes behind. Show your equation, solve the problem and check your work.

Solution:

$X + 15 = 120$

$X = 120 - 15$

$X = 105$ days

Check: 105 days would give 105 seconds. 105 seconds plus the initial 15 seconds would equal 120 seconds, which is two minutes.

Problem 4:

Simplify the following expression:

$$\frac{A^{11/4} \text{ x } A^{5/4}}{A^{3/4}}$$

Solution:

This is probably not a fair question because you may or may not have had power fractions in math prior to algebra. So in this case we will show you the solution and then give you the rule and then give you another question like this one.

First, $\mathbf{A^{11/4} \text{ x } A^{5/4} = A^{16/4}}$

Then if you divide by a power, you bring it up and the power becomes a minus power and you multiply it which means you add a minus number, which means you subtract it.

So $A^{16/4-3/4} = A^{13/4}$ So the correct answer is $A^{13/4}$

Reminder: Rules for exponents

A^x times A^y is equal to A^{x+y}
A^x divided by A^y is equal to A^{x-y}

Problem 5:

Simplify the following expression:

$$\frac{X^{3/8} \text{ x } X^{5/8}}{X^{3/4}}$$

Solution: First do the multiplication by adding exponents

$X^{3/8}$ x $X^{5/8} = X^{8/8}$

Then bring up the $X^{3/4}$ and it becomes $X^{-3/4}$

Then multiply $X^{8/8}$ x $X^{-3/4}$ which is the same as $X^{8/8}$ x $X^{-6/8}$

$X^{8/8}$ x $X^{-6/8} = X^{2/8}$ or $X^{1/4}$ Thus the answer is $X^{1/4}$

CHAPTER 4 GEOMETRY

FIRST: If you haven't already done so, go back and read the section on "The purpose of this book" and "The Introductory Overview" before you start. Most important, if you are a student, go back and read Chapter 2 "For Students". It's only 2 pages.

So what is Geometry really?

In a nutshell, it is the study of shapes and the mathematic means to describe and utilize these shapes for mankind.

Geometry is used in every aspect of life on a daily basis. It is used in machines, building construction, architecture, robotics, engineering, sports, art, sculpture, land surveys, space exploration, clothing, automobile design, and so much more. Geometry is used in one dimensional aspect like lines and in two dimensional shapes like a drawing of a triangle and 3 dimensional figures like the pyramids in Egypt.

Objective of this section of the book on Geometry.

There is only one objective to this section of the book. That is to provide you with the insight and the methods and techniques to get an A in Geometry. If you have read the two page chapter "For Students" you will know why. Even if you only obtained a C in Algebra, you can obtain an A in Geometry if you read this overview of Geometry and – if you practice the problems presented, and use the method and technique to be described in this chapter before starting your Geometry course.

What you do now will make all the difference when you sit down on your first day of Geometry class in your high school. This book is designed to provide just the right amount of material to keep the student's attention without overwhelming him or her with too much material.

The ideal time to read this material and practice the problems and solutions is the summer before you take the course. It is also best to read and study this material in short intervals, perhaps a half hour at a time. Do the presented problems over and over. There are only 11, but they are comprehensive so that if you can do these you will be more than prepared. At the end of the chapter there are also five more problems for fun and added learning that I believe you will find very helpful. After you have seen the solution to a problem, come back to the problem the next day and try to do it without looking at the solution. The more you do this the more it will sink in and the greater your chance of an A in the course.

Things You Need to Know Before You Even Start.

1. Shapes

You will be working with many different shapes and how to mathematically describe these shapes. You will learn formulas and theorems. Some will have to be memorized. All will require problem solving. There will be some algebra involved, but it is simple algebra and should not be a problem for anyone who has already taken algebra and passed the course. We will introduce each shape and then present a few typical problems along with the rules that apply to these shapes that have to be memorized or understood. Some shapes have many different forms such as triangles. The four triangle shapes are:

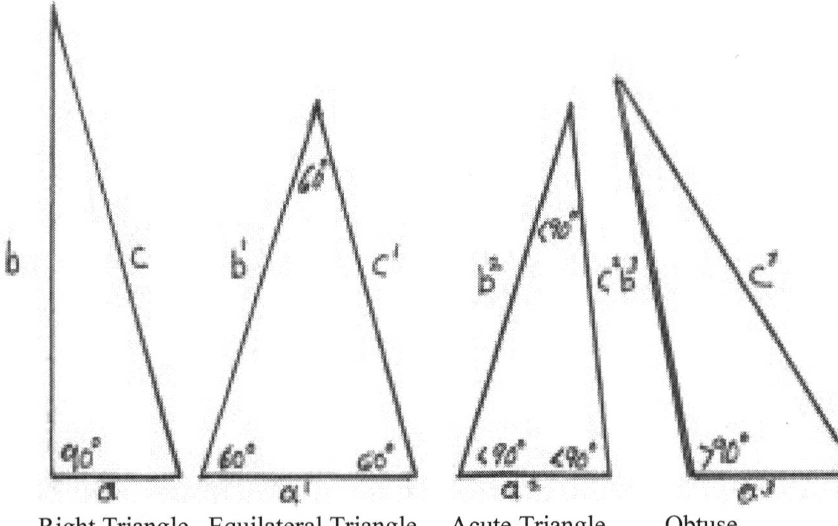

Right Triangle Equilateral Triangle Acute Triangle Obtuse Triangle

You will be working with these and definitely need to know what they are. We will cover more of this as we go through this treatise on Geometry. We will cover triangles first, then rectangles, then circles, and then spheres like cones and pyramids. When you finish this treatise on Geometry you will be ready to go into Geometry with a confidence that you are headed towards an A in the course.

2. Relationships

You will learn relationships between angles and line segments that may or may not be intuitive. However, the key is doing problems over and over. We will provide sample problems and solutions. Do these over and over until you feel comfortable with them. There won't be many problems, but they will be representative of the standard course in Geometry. Spending a little time now will make all the difference once you get in the classroom.

3. Typical Geometry problem.

So what does a typical Geometry problem look like. Here is one that you will encounter in some form in school and on final exams and college entrance tests, and in many job tests for technician type jobs in an industrial environment.

Right Triangle Problems:

Problem 1:

If triangle ABC is a right triangle and the two adjacent lines measure 6 inches and 8 inches respectively, what is the length of the third line segment.

Solution:

First draw and label the triangle described, which is a right triangle.
A right triangle is a triangle that has one of its angles at 90 degrees.
A degree is noted by a small zero in the upper right hand of the number.
So 90 degrees is written 90^0.

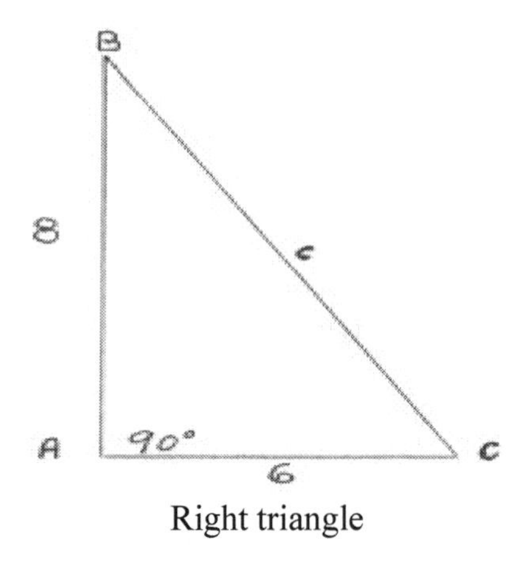

Right triangle

The adjacent lines to the 90^0 Angle should be labelled as 8 and 6 inches as shown above.

They are asking you for the segment c length, which is called the hypotenuse. The hypotenuse is always the line that is opposite the 90^0 angle. It is always the longest line segment.

In Geometry you will have to memorize the different types of triangles as well as certain formulas.

One of those formulas is the formula for determining the hypotenuse of a right triangle.

The formula is- the square of the hypotenuse is equal to the sum of the squares of the two adjacent sides. This is known as the Pythagorean Theorem. You can't pass Geometry without knowing this.

So using this formula;

$$c^2 = 8^2 + 6^2$$

$$c^2 = 64 + 36$$

$$c^2 = 100$$

Taking the square root of both sides

(Remember from Algebra you can do the same thing to both sides of an equation.) Thus you can take the square root of both sides and get:

c = 10 inches

Note: It is important to always label your answer. If it is inches, write inches. If it is degrees, write degrees. In textbooks degrees for angles will be noted with a small symbol at the upper right, like 90^0 means 90 degrees. You can use this symbol as well.

Before we go any further and discuss triangles and other configurations, it would be wise to provide a proven method that will make a student's efforts truly pay off in his life.

Method and technique to make an A in Geometry:

1. Get a notebook that is bound. One that you will not lose the pages. Also, purchase a pad of graph paper.
2. Take notes on one side of the page, leaving the other blank. You can take your notes on the right side or the left depending on which is easier for you. I always used the left side.
3. Purchase a good red marking pen.
4. As quickly after class as possible fix your illegible notes. I used to stay in the seat for 5 minutes before running to the next class. I would use my red pen to mark my notes so I could decipher them later on. When you are hurrying to take notes sometimes what seems clear when you are writing cannot be understood when you get home. But it is most likely still fresh in your mind right after class so you can write over in red a less than clear symbol or word that you wrote to make it clear for later.
5. Before you start any other homework copy your notes from one side of the page to the other. This reinforces what you have learned in class and makes it much neater. By having both pages side by side you can always refer to the original if you copied wrong. I always gave myself a treat when I started doing the copying. When I sat down to do Geometry I had a coke and a candy bar. It was my special time. Now a coke

and a candy bar would give me heartburn, but I was younger then.

6. After you have copied your notes, then do your Geometry homework problems. **DO THEM ALL.** Don't be lulled into false security because they seem redundant. Some may be redundant and some may have just a slight trick to them that you would not have caught if you skipped the problem.
7. Check your answers. If you got it wrong, fix it and highlight it in yellow. If you can't figure it out and have struggled with it, then the next day in class the light will shine when your teacher goes over it. But do your best to struggle if necessary to figure it out.
8. Highlight the problems that you missed.
9. Redo the highlighted problems that you missed first time.
10. Write down in red on the problem itself any questions you might have so you can ask them in class.
11. Now you are ready for class.
12. The teacher will likely go over homework and then present new material. If you have done everything above, you will find that it is just refreshing to go over the homework problems that you have already done.
13. Don't get cocky.
14. When you study for your test do practice problems from your homework, especially the ones that were highlighted in yellow. If you miss one, mark it in some way and do it again before the test.
15. This next item can very well make the difference between a B and an A. Many teachers will give students their test back. So if you can find someone from the previous year who still has their tests, get their tests and make sure you can do every problem on it. The teacher will not give the same test to you, but knowing how to do the previous year's test is a great way to help know what the teacher considers important. It is a great learning tool. Don't shirk on this one. Find someone who has taken these tests.
16. Smile when your paper comes back with a nice high mark. Because if you follow the above this is what is going to happen.

17. When you do well be prepared for your friends and peers to give you a hard time. Just tell them you find Geometry fun just like a video game. That should shut them up. Don't let them discourage you or make you feel bad for doing well. Just know that they are jealous and would never admit it. Ten years from now when you have the nice home, the great car and boat, and the great significant other, what they think now will be totally insignificant and meaningless.
18. One last thing–Don't miss one class. You can catch up in history or English, but Geometry is tough. It's probably 10 times harder than history. If you have to be out sick, try to come in for the Geometry class and then go back home. Your parents can write you a note. If you are in sports, try to fix your schedule to take Geometry in the morning so that you are not pulled out at the end of the day for a game or game practice. Some schools like to have special programs where a student leaves class for something. Don't get talked into skipping out on Geometry.

Note: When doing homework, some may find that it works better to do it in pieces. Do some now, then take a break, and then come back to it. This is especially true if you hit a wall and can't figure it out. And you will hit walls. Everyone does. It's like going from one level to the next in a video game. When you do hit a wall, take a deep breath and try again or go onto the next problem and then come back to this tough one later. You could also take a break and then come back fresh. Taking a walk around the block is a great break. Or shooting a couple of hoops. Even doing a couple of pushups is good because it puts oxygen in your brain. Whatever works for you is best. The physical activity is good because it negates the coke and candy bar potential weight gain.

Triangles:

Triangles make up a major portion of Geometry so we will start with triangles first. Let's look more closely at the four shapes introduced earlier. First we will discuss things relative to these four and then we will proceed with each triangle as a separate entity. So here again are the 4 different triangle types in Geometry.

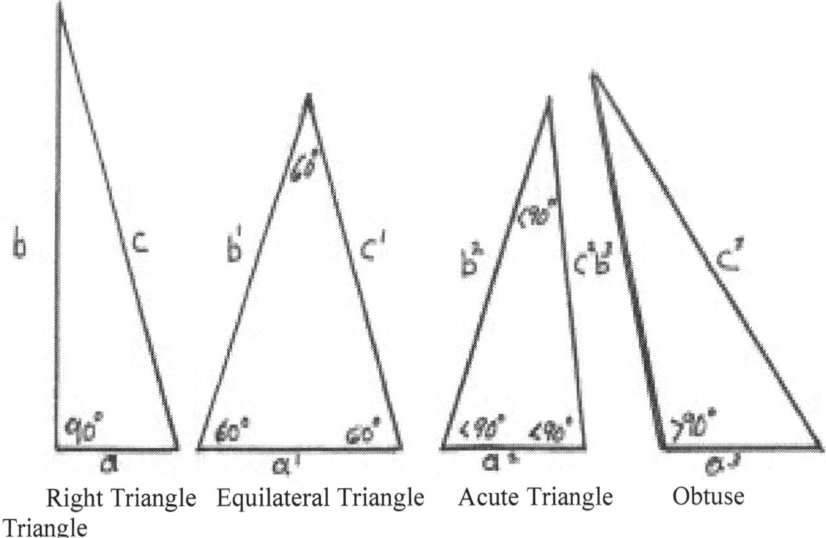

Right Triangle Equilateral Triangle Acute Triangle Obtuse Triangle

(Isosceles Triangle)

Right triangle: The definition of a right triangle is that it must have one angle equal to 90 degrees written as 90^0.

Equilateral triangle: The definition of an equilateral triangle is that all angles must be 60^0. Because all angles are the same 60^0 all three sides are the same length. So side a^1 is the same as b^1 and c^1 and then obviously b^1 and c^1 are also the same length. The equilateral triangle does not look from the drawing as though the sides are equal. This may happen to you on a test where they show the drawing and purposely don't have it look equal. However, you just know all sides are equal because all the angles are 60^0. You have to know this in Geometry. It's just a fact of physical laws, which we will explain further.

Isosceles triangle: You will note that under the Equilateral Triangle is the term Isosceles Triangle. By definition an Isosceles Triangle is one in which two sides are equal. In geometry the word congruent is used for equal. So that the definition is going to say that two sides are congruent. It could also have said that two angles of the triangle are equal because if the sides are equal so are the angles opposite the sides. So an equilateral triangle is also an isosceles triangle. But an isosceles triangle is not necessarily an equilateral triangle because the third side of an isosceles triangle could be different.

Isosceles right triangle: An isosceles right triangle would mean that two of the angles are 45^0 and the third of course is 90^0. This is because the sum of the angles of any triangle is always 180^0 and also because a right triangle must have one angle equal to 90^0. We will cover this in more depth later in the chapter.

Acute triangle: The definition of an acute angle is that all angles are less than 90^0 as shown symbolically by $< 90^0$.

Obtuse triangle: The definition of an obtuse triangle is that one angle must be greater than 90^0 ($> 90^0$ as shown in the pictorial).

30-60-90 Triangle ABC has a 30^0, 60^0, and a 90^0 angle and is called a 30-60-90 triangle. What makes this right triangle significant is the side lengths are always proportion no matter what size the triangle is. The ratio is always 1, 2, $\sqrt{3}$.

The 1 would be across from the 30 degree angle, the 2 would be across from the 90 degree angle and the $\sqrt{3}$ would be across from the 60 degree angle. We will do a problem later that demonstrates this.

Scalene triangle: A scalene triangle is one in which all 3 sides are different lengths. Since they are different lengths so are all 3 angles different sizes. Obviously an equilateral triangle cannot be scalene. The others may or may not be.

Polygon: All of the above shapes are polygons. A polygon is any two dimensional shape that has straight sides. Thus a circle is not a polygon because it does not have straight sides. Triangles, rectangles, etc. are two dimensional shapes that have straight sides. A one dimensional item would be a straight line because it has length, but no width. A three dimensional object is like a cone or a box or a pyramid because it has width and depth.

Let's talk about triangles in general. The first thing of importance about triangles is that every triangle has 180^0. If you add all three angles together they will always equal 180^2. It is obvious that the equilateral triangle has 180^0 because it has been labelled for you and you can add the three 60^0 angles and get 180^0. The right triangle only has a label at one angle and all you know about the acute triangle is that all angles are less than 90^0. You also only know that the obtuse angle has one angle greater than 90^0. However, all these triangles have a total of 180^0.

Most textbooks don't explain why they all add to 180^0, but just tell you this and expect you to just remember it for the rest of your life and for tests in class, on finals and on exams for college and some industrial job tests.

You are going to have to know the number of degrees in several shapes in Geometry from triangles to hexagons (six sided figure) to spherical objects, etc. I am going to take the time to give you an explanation that will help you in your course with geometric shapes. It all starts with the circle.

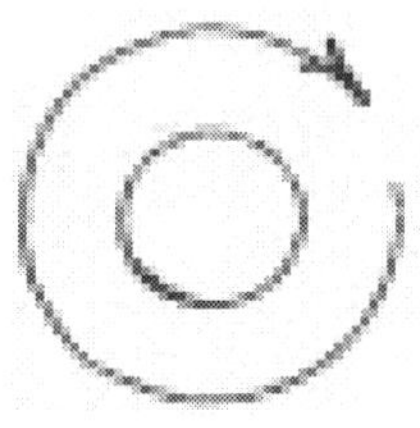

360^0 around circle

An ancient civilization known as the Babylonians divided a circle into 360 equal parts and called them degrees. They were obsessed with the number 60 so they had 6 times 60 or 360 in a circle. They had 60 seconds in a minute and 60 minutes in an hour.

They then must have done some experimenting and found that if you put a square in a circle it also had 360 degrees having 90 degrees on each corner. They then drew a diagonal across two corners of a square and/or a rectangle making two equal triangles. They discovered that each half logically had half of the square's number of degrees and so it was 180 degrees in a triangle.

They then manipulated (most likely) the triangle into every contortion that they could and found out no matter how they contorted it, the total number of degrees in any shaped triangle always equaled 180. If you want to try this manipulation you can go on line to **Triangles – Math Is Fun Virtual Manipulative**. Just put it into Google. Use the one that says triangle manipulative. It gives angles and triangle names for any of the manipulations that you make by dragging on the angle. You'll see and it's fun and informative.

Somewhere along the line, a protractor was invented that measured the angle in degrees. In a six sided hexagon that is a regular hexagon in that all sides and thus all angles are equal, each angle is 120^0 for a total of 720^0. It actually doesn't matter if the angles and sides are equal or unequal in size, the sum of the angles will always be 720^0. In a hexagon of unequal lengths, some of the angles will be more than 120^0 and some will be less, but the total will always be 720^0.

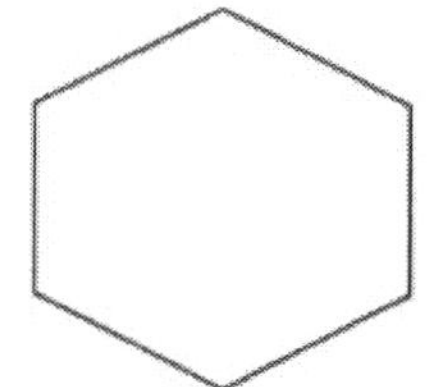

Regular hexagon
(Equal side lengths)

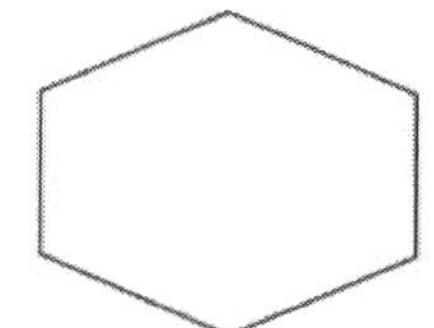

Hexagon with unequal sides

If you have a protractor you could check it out. You could also go back to the different triangles and measure all their angles and add them and discover that the sum of all three angles always equals 180^0. You can almost visualize taking the regular hexagon and squishing it down to look like the Hexagon with unequal sides and see that the total of all the angles will still remain the same. Some will have gotten bigger and some smaller.

Getting back to triangles, if a triangle has two equal angles, then the sides opposite these angles would be of equal length. For instance, if a right triangle has two 45^0 angles both sides opposite these two angles will be the same length.

The area of any triangle is equal to ½ the base times the height. The base is the side perpendicular to the height. Think of it as a capital L. The vertical leg is the height and the horizontal is the base. In the case of a right triangle (see drawing) line b is the height and line a is the base. In the case of other types of triangle, you will have to draw a line to make a height. We will explain later.

Alright, let's start by looking at rules and problems for right triangles.

Right Triangles:

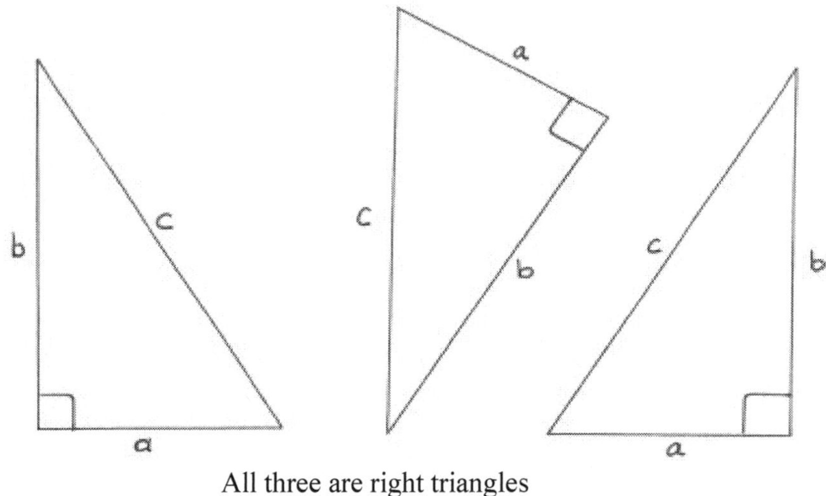

All three are right triangles

On tests and in math books, the right triangle may be shown in many different contortions with many different sized lengths. You must recognize that as long as it has a 90^0 angle, it is a right triangle. Whenever I had a test question involving a right triangle, I always drew it to where the 90^0 degree angle was to the left and on the bottom like the first drawing. It just seemed easier to work with.

Perimeter of a Right Triangle:

The perimeter of **<u>any</u>** triangle is defined as the sum of the sides. If the sides of a right triangle are :

a = 6 inches
b = 8 inches
c = 10 inches

then the perimeter is 6 + 8 + 10 = 24 inches.

Area of a Right Triangle:

We already have given this formula (known as the Pythagorean Theorem) as: the square of the hypotenuse is equal to the sum of the square of each of the other sides. This is only true for a right triangle unlike the perimeter formula that is true for all triangles.

Right Triangle Problems and Solutions:

Problem 2: Sometimes you will get an easy one like this:

One side of a 3 sided polygon is 15 feet. What is its perimeter if all angles are 60^0 ?

Okay, so we know it is a triangle because it has 3 sides.
We also know it is an equilateral triangle because all 3 angles are 60^0.
Thus all 3 sides are the same length.
Since we know the formula for perimeter is the sum of the three sides:

$$15 + 15 + 15 = 45 \text{ feet.}$$

Problem 3 Sometimes you will be lucky and it will be multiple choice.

If a right triangle has one of its sides adjacent to the hypotenuse at 8 feet in length what is the perimeter?
Round to the nearest foot.

Choices:

A. 24 feet
B. 48 feet
C. 27 feet
D. None of the above

Solution:

It is always best to make a drawing:

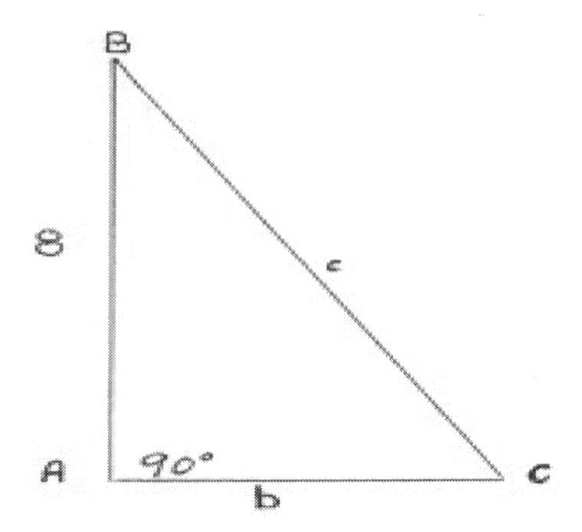

This drawing is what the problem told us

We know that if one of the angles is 45^0, then the other must also be 45^0

$$90^0 + 45^0 + 45^0 = 180^0$$

So if the other angle is 45^0, then its side must be the same

So you can redraw the triangle with the two 45^0 angles and the additional length of 8 for line segment AC.

Incidentally, in Geometry a line segment is written with a line over the

top like this:

$\overline{AC}$

For the purposes of this book, we will just call it AC

So now we need the length of c or line segment BC.

Since it is a right triangle

$$c^2 = 8^2 + 8^2$$

$$c = 11.3$$

So the perimeter is 8 + 8 + 11.3 = 27.3

Rounded to the nearest whole number = 27 feet

Thus c is the correct answer.

Problem 4 Some problems are more complicated.

Find the perimeter of right triangle ABC. Side BC is the hypotenuse. Side AB is 12 feet. The area of ABC is 54 square feet.

Solution:

Make a drawing and label what you know

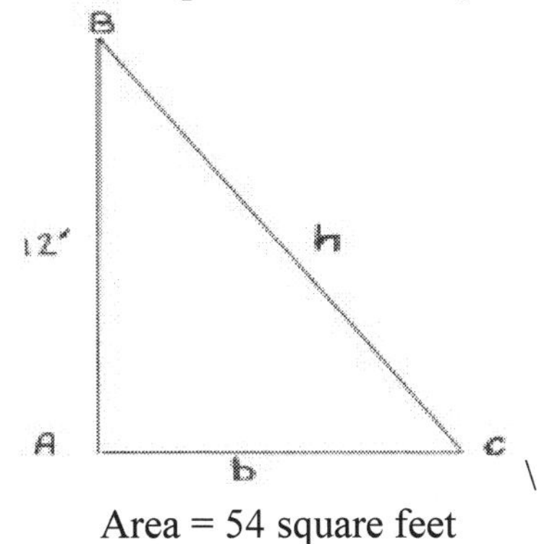

Area = 54 square feet

Area = ½ base x height

Area = 1/2b x 12

Or rewriting it

Area = 1/2x12b

54 = 6b

b= 9

Remember in algebra you can always check by plugging the number back in as follows:

$\frac{1}{2}(9)(12) = 54$ so it checks

You could now replace the b on the drawing with 9

So now all you have to do is find c

We know from the Pythagorean Theorem,

The hypotenuse of a right triangle is equal to the sum of the squares of the other two sides.

$$c^2 = 12^2 + 9^2$$

$$c^2 = 225$$

$$c = 15$$

So the perimeter = 9 + 12 + 15 = 36 feet

So what's the point of all this geometry stu*ff*?

Let's just take a simple example of a farmer who has a limited budget and cannot afford to purchase too much seed or fertilizer.

Problem 5:

Farmer Brown has a rectangular patch of ground that he wants to plant corn on. He needs to buy seed. The seed package says that the package can plant an area of 30 square feet. He walks down the long side of the patch and finds it measures 20 feet and then he walks down the shorter side and it is 12 feet. How many packages of seed does Farmer Brown need to purchase? Set up an equation and solve the problem.

Okay, first we remember the area of a rectangle is

A = LW, where

A = Area
L = Length
W = Width

But they want to know how many seed packages are in this area So we know that one package can handle an area of 30 square feet

Let's let P = the number of packages of Seed
Then P = A/30

So substituting LW for A we get

P = LW/30- this is the equation for the problem

Circle this and label it your equation because part of the word question asked you to set up an equation. Actually setting up the equation is what would be the biggest part of the grade for this question. So to finish the word problem,

P = (20 x 12)/30

P = 240/30

P = 8 packages of seed

Note: Always label your answer. In this case it was packages of seed. It is a good practice because it will make sure you answered the question and some teachers actually take off for failing to label. Sometimes the word question will say 2 points for the equation and 1 for the answer for a total of 3 points for this test question. So make sure you label the equation as your equation for the problem.

What if this had been a circular area he wanted to patch and he only knew how much it was to cross the distance from one point on the circle to a point straight across on the circular piece of land?

Well, in geometry you will get a formula to do this, which we will cover when we hit circles. If the land had been a right triangle and he knew the base and the height, we now know we can handle this as well. If it had been another kind of triangle, we could handle that as well. In fact, when you finish Geometry you could do any kind of shape even if you have to separate into pieces.

This example is just the tip of the iceberg. There are so many more reasons to learn geometry. In fact, I have used Geometry in my work and in my hobbies all my life. When I added a two story garage to my home, I did all the work myself. I used geometry to put in the stairs and to make a special roof that had a dormer window. Without a knowledge of geometry I could not have figured it out.

Getting a satellite in place requires weeks and even years of geometric calculations. Getting the first astronaut on the moon and getting astronauts to dock properly with a space station takes mammoth amounts of geometry. Putting up a skyscraper takes mammoth calculations so the building won't collapse or be affected by hurricanes and tornadoes. GPS is a major use of Geometry.

Other very serious reasons for doing well in Geometry are:

1. Better paying career job out of high school.
2. For those going to college, doing well in math and science will provide opportunity for serious scholarship money. See the attached article from my local Birmingham paper about scholarships. The attached news article shows the amount for grade average and ACT scores (college entrance tests). For an ACT of 30 and a score of B+ in high school, the scholarship pays $ 9,000 per year. Even a B average qualifies. With a B and an ACT of 24 you get $3,500 per year according to the article. You have to be an Alabama resident or live in certain counties in Florida and Mississippi to qualify. Most every state has similar programs for residents of their state.
3. Doing well in Geometry will help you dramatically in Trigonometry and in the Sciences because they all use Geometry.
4. Doing well in Geometry and then the other math and sciences will open up doors (even if you don't go to college) in many fields like medicine (from technicians to doctors), engineering, computer programming, technicians in all fields, technical maintenance of high tech equipment, technical sales, and much more. A programmer will have to know Algebra and Geometry because he will be called upon to write programs that include formulas and equations (Algebraic and Geometric) some that he may have to develop.
5. Getting into two year technical schools. Technical schools let students go right into high tech jobs that pay well and are extremely interesting. Industry is crying for these graduates and paying to get them. Many industries will provide tuition assistance to their employees to go to these schools. The key is to do well in science and math.
6. Geometry will improve the math skills that you missed in earlier courses. You will learn many of the things you had trouble with in the past. Just keep a red pen to mark those things that you have

forgotten as you come to them in Geometry. Call them rules and memorize them. One of the best ways to memorize is to practice these rules with the problems given to you for homework.

7. Geometry teaches you about reasoning and logical thinking and improves your spatial concept of the world. It allows you to improve your mental muscles just like an athlete must work his physical muscles to compete in the world.

These are the scholarships listed from the University of South Alabama for Alabama residents plus Mississippi students from George, Greene, Harrison, Jackson, Perry and Stone Counties and Florida students from Escambia and Santa Rosa counties.

ACT Composite Score	SAT Equivalent (SAT Critical Reading + Math)	Minimum High School GPA	Annual Amount	4 Year Total Amount
33 or higher	1440 or higher	3.5	$11,000	$44,000
32	1400-1430	3.5	$9,000	$36,000
30-31	1330-1390	3.5	$8,000	$32,000
28-29	1250-1320	3.5	$5,000	$20,000
24-27	1090-1240	3.0	$3,500	$14,000

23	1050-1080	3.0	$2,500	$10,000

ACT Composite Score	SAT Equivalent (SAT Critical Reading + Math)	Minimum High School GPA	Annual Amount	4 Year Total Amount
33 or higher	1440 or higher	3.5	$12,000	$48,000
32	1400-1430	3.5	$10,000	$40,000
30-31	1330-1390	3.5	$9,000	$36,000
28-29	1250-1320	3.5	$6,500	$26,000
27	1210-1240	3.5	$5,000	$20,000

Two more Triangle Problems:

Problem 6 Isosceles Triangle

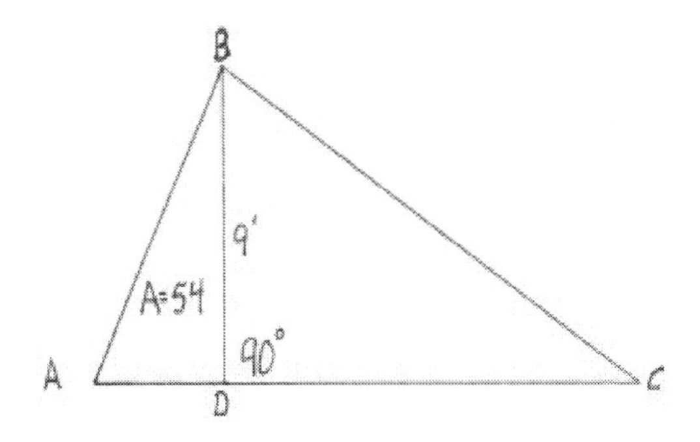

The isosceles triangle ABC shown has an area of 54 feet for right triangle ABD. Find the perimeter of DBC. The height (sometimes referred to as the altitude) is 9 feet. Line segment AC is 30 feet.

Solution: They drew this one for us. However they did not write in the distance from A to C, but told us it was 30 feet. We should write this in ourselves. We can add the dimension of the sides as we determine them.

First, we note that angle ADB is a right angle. We know this because we were told in our Geometry book that the arc on any point on a line is 180^0. This is quite logical because if you took two right triangles and laid them back to back like the figure above the two 90^0 angles would add to 180^0.

So first let's solve for line segment AD.

Since Area = ½ Base x Height

54 = ½ AD x 9

½ AD = 6

AD = 12

Also by the Pythagorean Theorem we know that

The hypotenuse $(AB)^2 = 9^2 + 12^2$

$(AB)^2 = 225$

AB = 15 and DC = 18 by subtracting 12 from 30

Let's add the numbers to the drawing to see where we are:

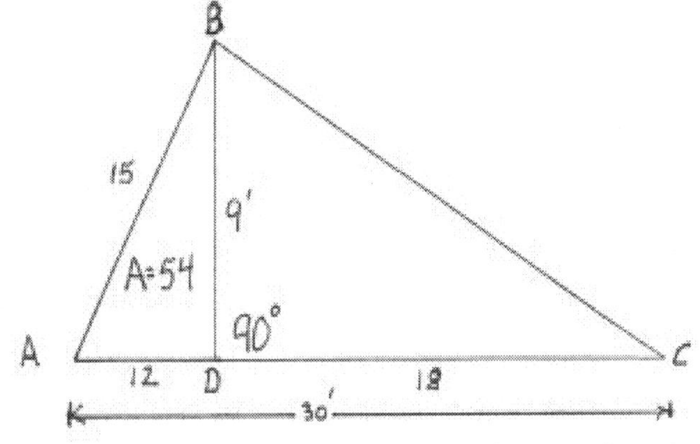

So we still need BC to obtain the perimeter of DBC

You probably know what comes next by now

$(BC)^2 = 9^2 + 18^2$

$(BC)^2 = 81 + 324$

BC = 20.1

So the perimeter of DBC = 9 + 20.1 + 18 = 47.1 feet.

Be careful. Don't get perimeter and area mixed up.

***Problem** 7* The 30-60 -90 Triangle

Line segment AB has a length of 10 feet. What is the perimeter and area of triangle ABC?

Solution:

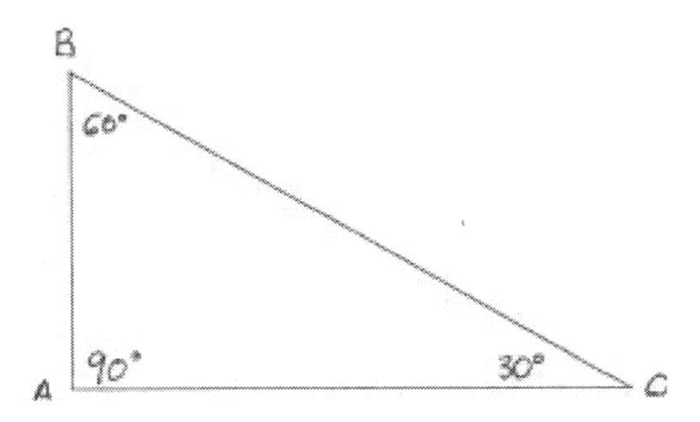

Solving this problem requires the definition of a 30-60-90 triangle. A 30-60-90 triangle always has the sides in the following ratio:

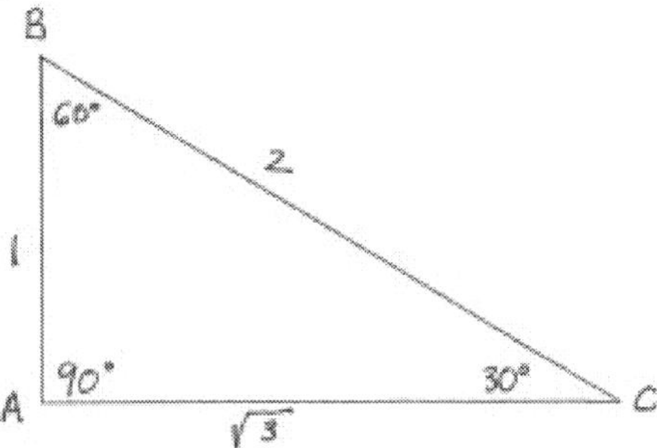

Solution:

Side AB was given as 10 and therefore side BC is 20 feet.

Side AC is equal to $\sqrt{3}$ x 10

$\sqrt{3} = 1.732$

1.732 x 10 = 17 rounded to nearest whole number

Perimeter = 10 + 20 + 17 = 47 feet

Area = ½ 10 x 17

Area = 85 square feet (ft^2)

Rectangles:

The definition of a rectangle is that all angles are 90^0. A square is a rectangle in which all the sides are equal as well as all the angles being 90^0. Area of a rectangle is the Length x Width (L x W). The perimeter is 2L + 2W or 2(L + W).

Problem 8:

Given that a rectangle has a perimeter of 30 and an area of 50 what is the length and width of this rectangle?

Solution:

Let the length = L
Let the width = W
Perimeter = P
Area = A

A = L x W
P = 2L + 2W
Thus L x W = 50

2L + 2W = 30 or 2(L + W) = 30

2W = 30 -2L

W = 15 – L

Substituting into the Area Equation for W

$$L \times (15-L) = 50$$

Multiply by -1 and rearrange to = 0

$$15L - L^2 - 50 = 0$$

Or

$$(L - 10)(L + 5) = 0$$

Thus L = 10 or -5 or both

Let's let L = 10 feet

Then W must equal 5 feet because 10W = 50

Checking:

$$P = 2(5 + 10)$$

P = 30 feet and so it checks

So the correct answer is:

L = 10 feet
W = 5 feet

Circles

Circles are given by two formulas;

$C = \pi d$, where

C = circumference (fancy word for perimeter
$\pi = 3.14$
d = diameter (line across the center of the circle connecting two points across from each other on the circumference of the circle)

And
$A = \pi r^2$, where

A = area of the circle
$\pi = 3.14$ (sometimes given as 22/7)
r = radius (line from the center of the circle to any point on the circumference)

π is a symbol called Pi and pronounced just like in apple pie and is the ratio of the circumference of a circle to the diameter. No matter how big the diameter and thus the circle, this number of 3.14 for the ratio is always the same.

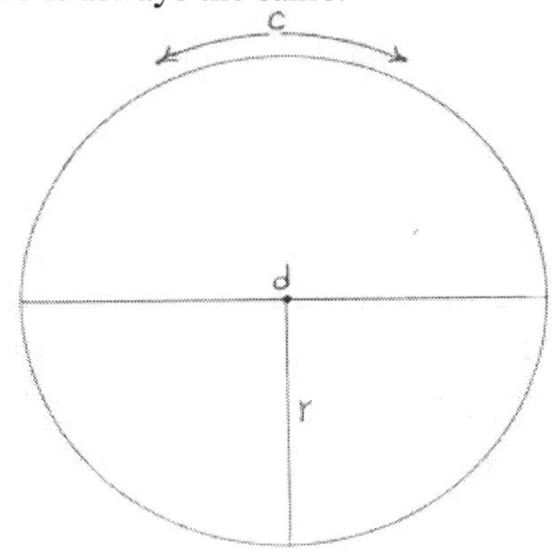

c = circumference (distance around like a perimeter for a rectangle)
d = diameter of the circle (the dot below the "d" is the center)
r = radius of the circle
$c/d = \pi = 3.14$ or 22/7

Note: **2r = d**

Problem 9: Real life recent problem

My wife asked me for help while she was making a bolster pillow. A bolster pillow is a tubular pillow that you see on a sofa or at the head of a bed for decoration. She needed to know how much material she needed to go around in a circle around a diameter of 10 inches.

I knew from geometry that the circumference of a circle was given by the formula—πd. The symbol π is Greek and pronounced pie just like apple pie. Π is simply a ratio of circumference to diameter and is equal to 3.14 as mentioned already. For every inch in diameter, there is 3.14 inches in circumference going around the circle. (The circumference is the circle around a center point.) Thus I was able to tell my wife without even having to think or use paper that she needed ten times 3.14 or 31.4 inches of yarn to go around the 10 inch diameter. She rounded off and cut 31 and a half inches and it was just fine. The bolster pillow turned out well and my wife thinks I am really smart (sometimes).

Problem 10:

Find the area of the shaded section in the upper left hand corner given that the circumference of the circle is 314 feet.

Solution:

Since the circumference = πd

$$314 = 3.14d$$

$$d = 100$$

d is also the distance of the side of the square in the box. We know it's a square because the diameter will always be the same no matter where it is across the circle. So both the base and width of the square are 100 feet.

Since A = LW for a square (or any rectangle)

$$A = 100 \times 100$$

$$A = 10{,}000 \text{ ft}^2$$

We now have the area of the square

If $d = 100$ then $r = 50$

Since $A = \pi r^2$ for a circle

$A = 3.14\ (50)^2$

$A = 7{,}850\ ft^2$
So now we have the areas of both the square and the circle

Subtracting the area of the circle from the square

$10{,}000 - 7{,}850 = 2{,}150\ ft^2$

Since the shaded portion is equal in size to the other 3 identical corners

The shaded section is ¼ of the total $2{,}150\ ft^2$ or $537.5\ ft^2$

So the correct answer is $537.5\ ft^2$

Three Dimensional Objects or Spheres

Volume for three dimensional objects or spheres are going to be to the third power because you are multiplying three dimensions. Two dimensional drawings had an area rather than a volume and were squared because there were only two dimensions.

Volume of Prisms, Cylinders, and Boxes

Prisms, cylinders, and boxes all have the same volume formula:

$V = Ah$, where

V = volume
A = Area
h = the height or altitude of the area

Problem 11

What is the volume of the prism shown in the drawing?

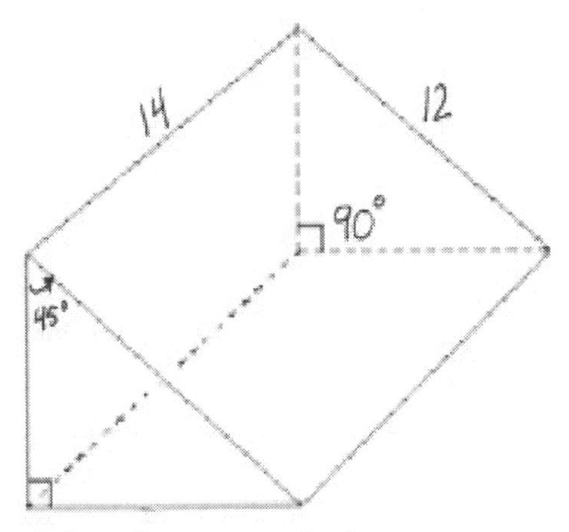

Prism distances are in feet

Solution:

First we need to realize that a prism is just a triangle extended some distance, in this case 14 feet

It is always best to draw the basic unit, which in this case is the triangle
(If it were a cylinder, the circle would be the basic unit extended out some distance,
If it were a box, it would be the length and width that was extended some distance.

Drawing the triangle and putting in what we know,

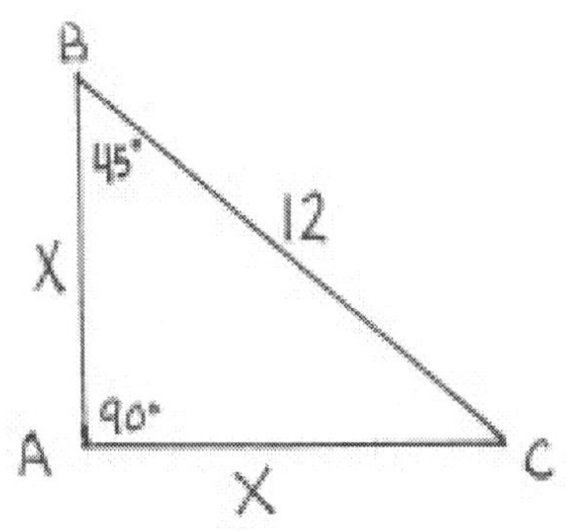

Since it is an Isosceles right triangle, the two sides are equal and have been labelled as X.

$$Area = 1/2X \times X$$

$$Area = 1/2X^2$$

We also know that the hypotenuse (12) squared is equal to the sum of the square of the other two sides, thus

$$144 = X^2 + X^2$$

$$2X^2 = 144$$

$$X^2 = 72$$

Plugging into Area = $1/2X^2$ we get,

$$Area = ½ (72)$$

Area = 36 ft^2 for the triangle

The length or altitude of the prism is 14 ft.

The volume is thus $36ft^2 \times 14ft = 504\ ft^3$

Some may have found it easier to understand to solve for X and then calculated the area as follows:

$$144 = X^2 + X^2$$

$$X^2 = 72$$

X = 8.5 ft. rounded from 8.485

So then the area would be

$$A = ½\ 8.5 \times 8.5$$

$$A = 36\ ft^2$$

The volume is thus $36ft^2 \times 14ft = 504\ ft^3$ either way

Other Geometric Figures:

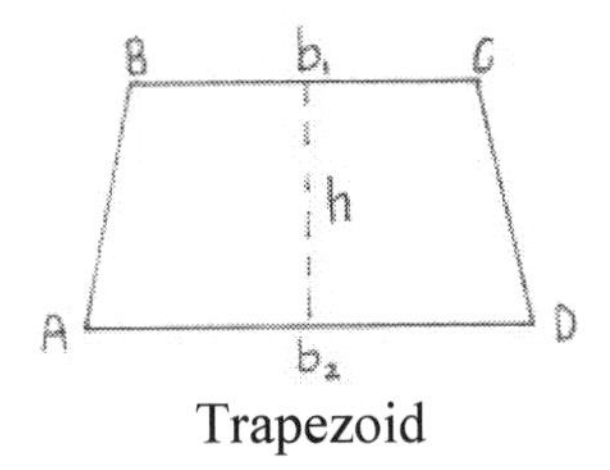

Trapezoid

Area = $(b_1 + b_2)/2 \times h$,
Where b_1 = line segment BC
b_2 = line segment AD

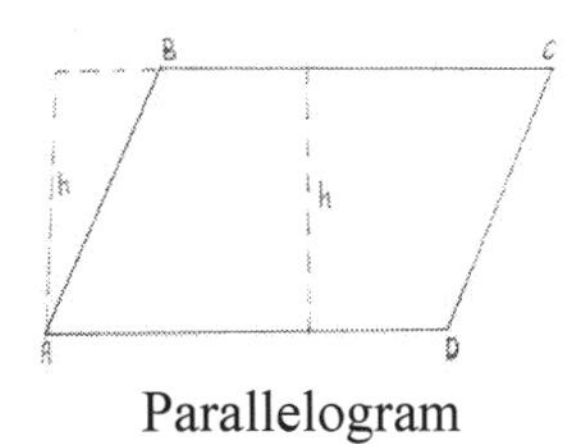

Parallelogram

Area = base x height,

where the base (BC and AD) are the same length. Either can be used for the base. What makes it a parallelogram is that the opposite sides are parallel to each other (same distance apart).

Problems with these two figures are basically the same as the other figures that have been used as examples.

Summary:

You now have a basic understanding of Geometry. You know what it is going to look like because you have now seen the Reader's Digest version that is the short version for the year-long course. Some of the examples shown to you were on a high level and some on a simple level. School will fill in the spaces between the simple and complex.

With practice this will become second nature. This overview will give you a leg up on doing well in Geometry. The biggest thing is practice, practice, practice. Just like in real estate it is location, location, location. The methods and techniques described in this book will net you an A if followed.

Remember, it's important to know how to use the equations. I have never seen a test in which a student was asked to derive a formula equation. If you go into higher math this may be valuable, but it is not necessary now. Remember, it isn't how to build an engine, it's how to drive the car and knowing the rules of the road.

Also, don't think because you were not good in math in the past that you are going to be poor in Geometry. This is definitely not the case. You could have been mediocre in math in the past and very well become an A student in Geometry. It's a whole new ball game.

Remember, this country needs more of you to go into math and science. It's where the jobs are going to be created. It's where the world can be made a better place and it's where the United States can stand tall amongst the other nations.

Best of luck and success to you,

John D. Forlini

Appendix A

Steps to Solve Word Problems:

1. First and foremost figure out what the problem wants from you. Sounds simple, but half the time this is where we fall down. Are they asking you for speed, numbers of kittens, or time. Whatever it is write it down and then give it a letter. For some reason most people like to use X. However, it is a great practice to use the letter that corresponds to what you are looking for.
2. Write down what units the answer should be in. Is it feet, square feet, or cubic feet, etc.
3. Ignore the unnecessary stuff in the word problem. Don't let stuff that is not essential confuse you.
4. If possible draw a picture that is representative of the question. Geometry questions lend themselves well to pictures.
5. Make a label (letter or number if given) for each item or variable.
6. Set up an equation or equations that satisfy the request and given information. Sometimes just putting the

problems words into an equation will give you the guidance to solve the problem as will a good drawing.

7. Put the equation or equations into its simple easy form. Put all the letters on one side and the numbers on the other. If it's more than one equation, try to manipulate them to look alike. Sometimes this will mean that you don't have all the letters on one side and all the numbers on the right. You will have to play with it.
8. You will always hit that awful problem that you just can't see how to do. Don't waste time on this one, go to the next one. Remember on an ACT entrance exam or other exam most of the time every problem has equal weight. So put this one aside for later. The brain is an amazing thing. Sometimes while you are working on other problems, your brain will be unconsciously working out the solution to the problem.
9. Check your work quickly by substituting your answer back into the original equation.

Key Words to Look For and their Algebraic Meaning:

1. The English words that denote (+) are sum, add, in addition, more than, and, increased, both, greater than, and plus. An example would be "5 more than X". This would be X + 5.
2. The English words that denote (–)are subtract, less than, decreased by, reduced by, difference, take away, diminished by, and deduct. An example would be "Difference between X and 5". The answer would be X-5. Be careful because "Difference between 5 and X" would be 5-X.
3. The English words that denote (x) are times, times as much, multiply, product, tax on, by, lots of, percent of, and interest on. The tax on goods in Hoover, Alabama is 9%. Tax = .09 x goods.
4. The English words that denote (/) are divided by, divide, quotient, goes into, per, and how many times. An example would be "Maximum five tickets per customer for each show. Show = 5/customer maximum. Five customers can get how many tickets? 5 x (5/C) or 25 tickets.

5. The English words that denote (=) are equal, is, result, will be, was, gives, yields, sold for, and produced. An example would be "Two scoops of cement mix and 500 pounds of gravel produced a ton of concrete." $2S + 500 = 2{,}000$ pounds. Note: one ton = 2,000 pounds. So $2S = 1{,}500$ and $S = 750$ pounds of cement mix per scoop. This assumes that the question asked how much each scoop weighed. There will be a few symbols in geometry. Just memorize them.

Some Geometry Symbols to know:

Right Angle ∟

Line Segment $\overline{AB}$

Perpendicular $\perp$

Angle $\angle$

Parrallel $\parallel$

Five More Geometry Problems for Fun

Five problems for fun and further learning are as follows:

Problem 1:

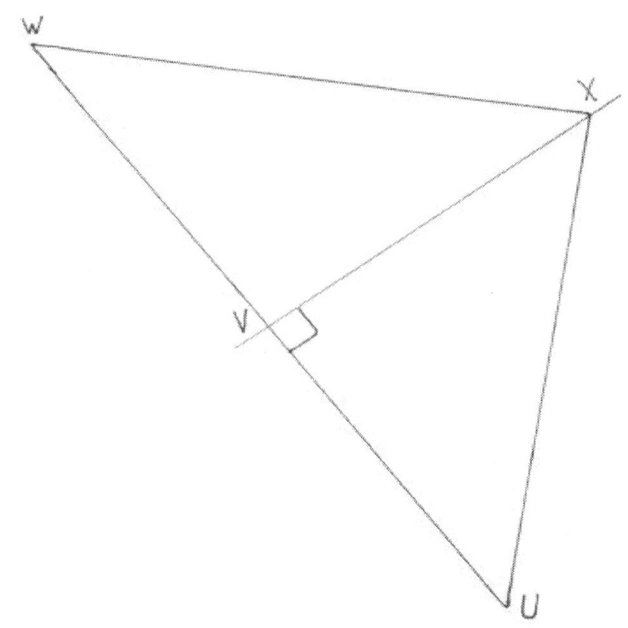

Triangle UWX was bisected through angle WXU.
Line segment WX is 15 feet.
Line segment UV is 9 feet.

What is the value of line segment XU?
What is the value of line segment VX?

Solution:

By symbolism, angle UVX is a 90^0 angle, therefore since angle WXU was bisected (two equal angles) then triangle UVX is congruent (same size) as triangle VWX.

Therefore XU is the same length as WX, which is 15 feet.

Since we know two sides of a right triangle, then the other side can be found from the Pythagorean theorem in which the square of the hypotenuse of a right triangle is equal to the sum of the squares of the other two sides.

$15^2 = 9^2 + (VX)^2$
VX = 12
Problem 2:

Given a triangle with coordinates A (-10, -8) , B (-10, -2) and C (-6,-2) find the new coordinates if you move the triangle up 10 points and over 14 points. Show a sketch of the triangles.

Solution:

First, sketch the requested starting points of the triangle as follows:

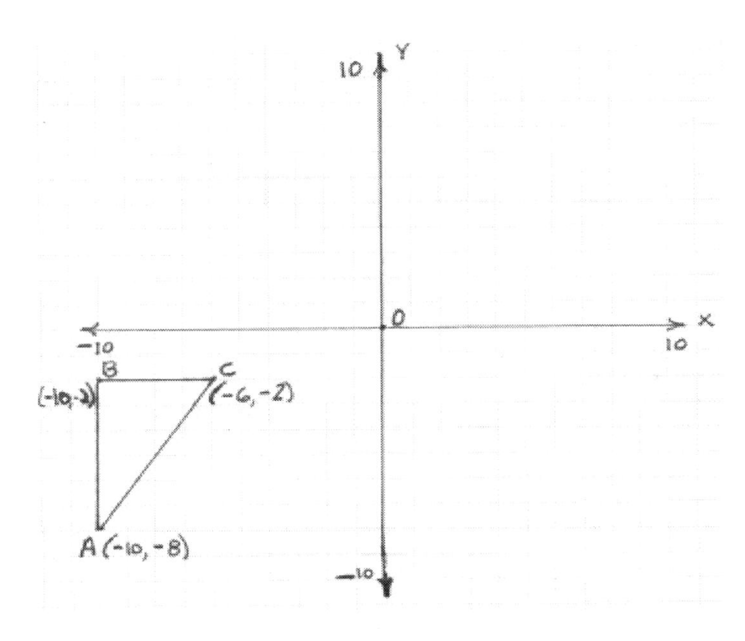

Then make a matrix from which to change the coordinates as follows:

A (-10, -8) > A′ (   )
B (-10, -2) > B′ (   )
C (-6, - 2) > C′ (   )

Reminder: (x,y) The x is first in the parenthesis followed by the y.

Thus up is an increase in the y axis and over is an increase in the x axis.

Let's do the x's first as follows by adding 14 to each x point:

A (-10, -8) > A' (4,)
B (-10, -2) > B' (4,)
C (-6, - 2) > C' (8,)

Then do the same with the y by adding 10 to each as follows:

A (-10, -8) > A' (4, 2)
B (-10, -2) > B' (4, 8)
C (-6, - 2) > C' (8, 8)

Now re-sketch with the new coordinates.

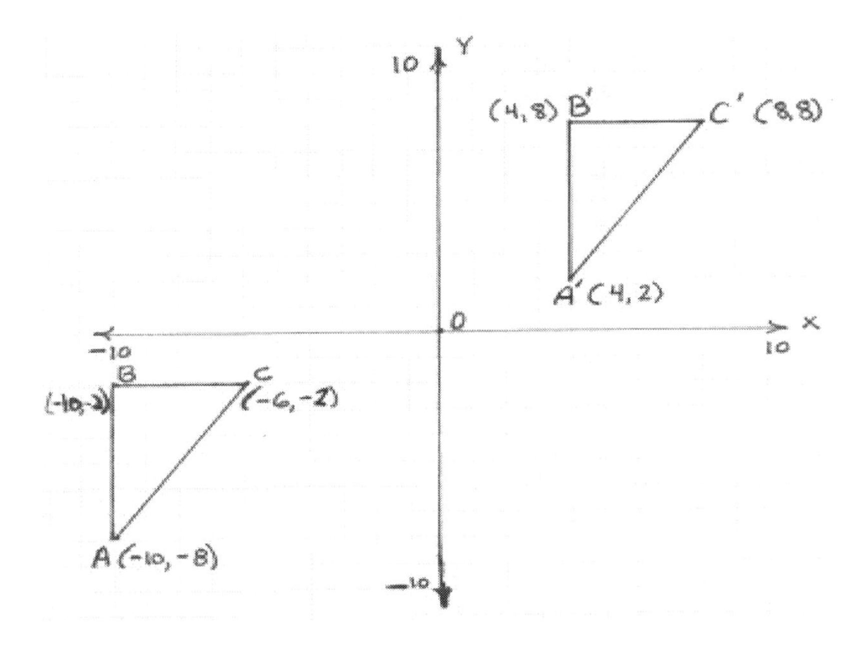

Problem 3:

In the above problem 2 determine the area of triangle $A'B'C'$. Is it the same as the area for triangle ABC?

Solution:

Obviously, this is a right triangle. The length of $A'B'$ is the distance on the y axis, which is simply 8-2 or 6 units. The length of $B'C'$ is simply 8-4 or 4 units. Thus we have the base at 4 and the height at 6.

Since the area of a right triangle = ½ bh,

then the area of triangle ABC = ½ 4 x 6 = 12 units

Regarding the second question " is the area the same as ABC", one would only have to look at the absolute lengths of $B'C'$ and $A'B'$, which are 4 and 6, thus the triangles have the same area.

Reminder: The absolute value of a number or value such as x as denoted by the symbol $|x|$ means the absolute value of x. This would also apply to an operation like subtraction. Thus the absolute value of the subtraction like $|-2 - (-8)| = 6$. Remember minus a minus is a plus. Thus $-2 - (-8)$ is really -2 plus 8 or 6 even without the absolute value symbol.

In the case of $|-10 - (-6)|$ the subtraction in the absolute value symbol is minus 4 which because it is in the absolute symbol then becomes 4 without the minus.

Problem 4:

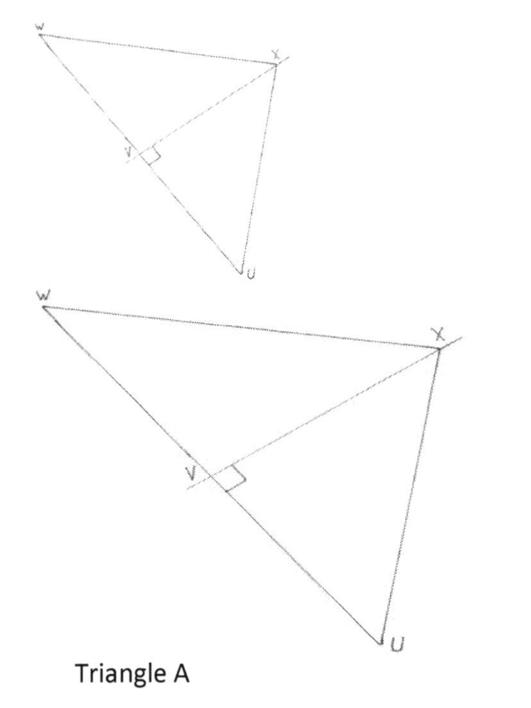

Triangle A Triangle B

Triangle A and triangle B are similar triangles. VX line segment bisects triangle B at points V and X on the triangle. If VX is 18 ft. in triangle B and VX is 9 ft. in triangle A, what is the area of triangle WXU in both triangles if WX in triangle A is 13.45 ft.

Note: Similar triangles means that they are similar if they have the same shape, but can be different sizes and rotation.

Solution:

First, sketch what you know from the problem.

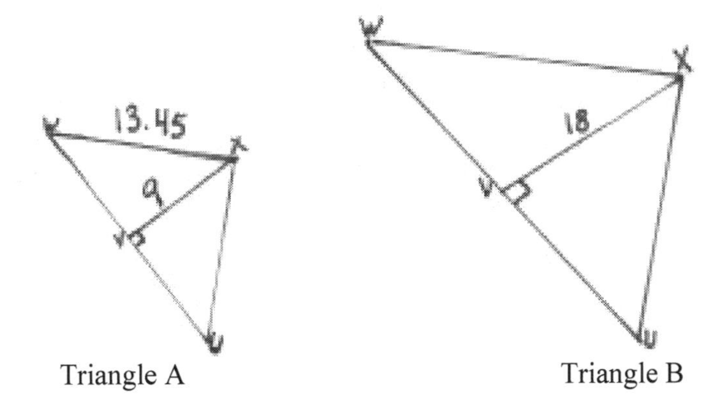

Triangle A Triangle B

Then, since we know that the triangles are similar we know that WX in triangle B has to be twice the size of WX from triangle A since VX is twice the size. Basically, if they are similar the sizes all have to be the same proportion.

If we can get the area of either of the triangles we can figure it out. So let's just work with triangle B. We could have just as easily worked with triangle A.

Since WX in triangle A is 13.45 ft., then WX in triangle B is 26.9 ft.

Since WX is the hypotenuse of a right triangle then:

$(26.9)^2 = (18)^2 + (WV)^2$

$724 = 324 + (WV)^2$

$(WV)^2 = 400$

WV = 20 ft.

Thus we know that WV is 20 ft. in triangle B and 10 ft. in triangle A.

We also know that the area of a triangle is ½ Base x Height.

Thus the area of triangle WXV in triangle B is:

$\frac{1}{2}$ 18 x 20 = 180 $ft.^2$

So now let's do the area of triangle WXV in triangle A as follows:

$\frac{1}{2}$ 9 x 10 = 45 $ft.^2$

Okay, you are wondering why it isn't twice as much. The answer is because you are squaring it. Try something simple like 2 and 4. Four is twice two, but $2^2 = 4$ and $4^2 = 16$, thus when you square a number that is twice its size the square becomes 4 times its size. Try several numbers and you will see this always works out. Try 5 and 10. The squares are 25 and 100, thus the square is always 4 times greater rather than twice.

So 180 $ft.^2$ is 4 times greater than 45 $ft.^2$.

Now, we still haven't answered the question. The question asked for the area of WXU in both triangles. Since we know the area of half of each triangle we simply double the area. Thus the answer is :
Area of WXU for triangle A is 90 $ft.^2$
Area of WXU for triangle B is 360 $ft.^2$

Problem 5:

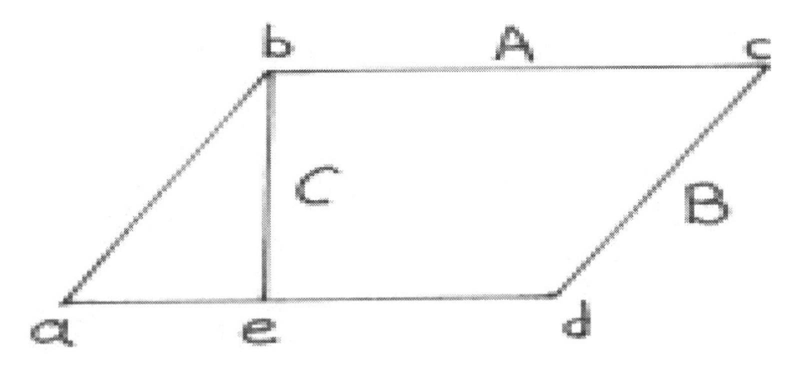

Figure abcd is a parallelogram. Side A is 20 ft. and side B is 15 ft. The area of triangle abe is 54 $ft.^2$. The length of line segment ed is 11 ft. Find the area of the parallelogram.

Solution:

First, look at the drawing and then put down what you know and then re-sketch.

B = 15 ft.
A = 20 ft.
ed = 11 ft.

From the above, we can deduce the following since parallel lines are equal:

ae = 9 ft. (20-11) and ab = 15 ft.

Re-sketching and putting in the numbers gives:

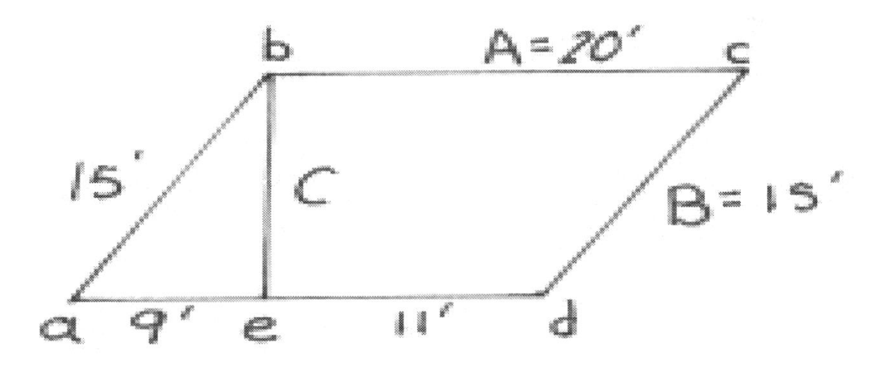

We know that the area of a parallelogram is equal to the base times the height. The base is 20 so all we need is the height C.

Using the Pythagorean theorem where $c^2 = a^2 + b^2$ or the hypotenuse squared is equal to the sum of the other two sides squared, we can solve for the height C.

The hypotenuse is 15 so $15^2 = 9^2 + C^2$

$225 = 81 + C^2$

$C^2 = 225 - 81$

$C^2 = 144$

C = 12 ft.

So the area of the parallelogram $= 12 \times 20 = 240$ ft.^{2}

Note: Do these problems over and over until they are second nature and you will do very well in your geometry class. You can probably see that each problem is a learning experience. Knowing what to do is not the same as actually doing it. It's like driving a car. You may know what to do, but until you actually drive in traffic and learn the rules of the road and learn to anticipate other driver's movements you really don't know how to drive.

It is the same with math and science. You have to practice, practice, and practice some more.

CHAPTER 5 CHEMISTRY

FIRST: If you haven't already done so, go back and read the section on "The purpose of this book" and "The Introductory Overview" before you start. Most important, if you are a student, go back and read Chapter 2 " For Students". It's only 2 pages.

So what is Chemistry really about?

In a nutshell, it is the study of what everything is made of and how different substances (both natural and manmade) react under different conditions. How they react to physical change and to each other. If you mix an acid and an alkali you get a violent reaction. If you heat water to its boiling point it changes to steam. If you mix two clear solutions they can suddenly become a bright red. If you mix two liquids together they can immediately take on a solid from.

Chemistry is a science that has given so much to the world from glass to steel to nylon to DNA. We are still in the infancy of what scientists can do with chemistry. Don't think for a minute that everything has been invented. Don't think for a minute that everything that has already been invented is as good as it can be. Every man made chemical can be improved. Every process that makes these chemicals can be improved. Chemistry is reducing the impurities in the atmosphere and manufacturing all kinds of medical and cosmetic products to make us look better.

After graduating with a degree in chemistry I spent years working with processes in plants that made heart medicines, agricultural growth and harvesting chemicals, pesticides, man-made fibers like polyester, and I have worked with processes that made paper, silicon chips for computers, and catalysts to enhance chemical reactions.

I was a superintendent of chemical labs with over 30 technicians that did testing and small development work. These technicians made good money. Only a few had college educations, but all had good math and science skills. Some came to work right out of high school and because of their doing well in math and science they were able to obtain these good paying jobs. We provided them with classroom learning in the plant as well as on the job training to enhance their knowledge and help them advance in job and pay.

Objective of this section of the book on Chemistry.

There is only one objective to this section of the book. That is to provide you with the insight and the methods and techniques to get an A in Chemistry. If you have read the two page chapter "For Students" you will know why. Even if you only obtained mediocre grades in earlier subjects, you can obtain an A in Chemistry if you read this overview of Chemistry and – if you practice the problems, and use the method and technique to be described in this chapter before starting your Chemistry course. This will give you the template for the course.

What you do now will make all the difference when you sit down on your first day of Chemistry class in your high school. This book is designed to provide just the right amount of material to keep the student's attention without overwhelming him or her with too much material.

The ideal time to read this material and practice the problems and solutions is the summer before you take the course. It is also best to read and study this material in short intervals, perhaps a half hour at a time. Do the presented problems over and over. There are only 12, but they are comprehensive so that if you can do these you will be more than prepared. After you have seen the solution to a problem, come back to the problem the next day and try to do it without looking at the solution. The more you do this the more it will sink in and the greater your chance of an A in the course.

Things You Need to Know Before You Even Start.

First thing you need to know is that Chemistry and the high school course in chemistry is divided into 2 distinct halves:

1. Inorganic Chemistry – Example – Sodium Chloride –

   NaCl

   NaCl is made up of Na^+ (sodium) and the element Cl^- chlorine. This is the salt in your salt shaker. In solid form like the salt in your salt shaker, NACL is bonded together. When mixed in water, these two elements break up into ions of Na^+ and Cl^-. We will explain what ions are shortly. Ions are the most important aspect of inorganic chemistry.

2. Organic Chemistry – Example – Alcohol – CH3CH2OH

```
 H H
 | |
H-C-C-OH
 | |
 H H
```

This alcohol molecule has two carbon atoms. Each carbon atom has the ability to bond with 4 other elements as long as they have a single bond opening. Some have double bond requirements such as O (Oxygen). Oxygen would use up two of carbon's 4 bonding positions. We will explain more later, but for now this is what an organic compound looks like. Each molecule has two carbon (C) atoms, 6 hydrogen (H) atoms, and one oxygen (O) atom. Get used to seeing it written in the two forms shown because you will see this type of presentation in organic chemistry.

So what is the difference and what is the significance?

The difference is that inorganic chemistry deals with all the elements in the periodic table (which we will discuss shortly) and organic chemistry has the element carbon as its main focal element as can be seen in item 2 Organic Chemistry.

The second thing you need to know are some of the significant terms that will be important throughout the course. We will list them now with definitions and then you will see them more clearly in this book as we go on. Some of these significant terms are:

Terms and definitions in Chemistry

Atom: An atom is the smallest unit of an element that cannot be broken down and cannot be separated into simpler substances. Singly and in combination they constitute all matter known in the universe. It is the defining structure of an element and cannot be broken by any chemical methods. An atom consists of a nucleus of protons and neutrons with electrons that orbit this nucleus. An atom is the smallest component of an element that still retains the chemical properties of that element.

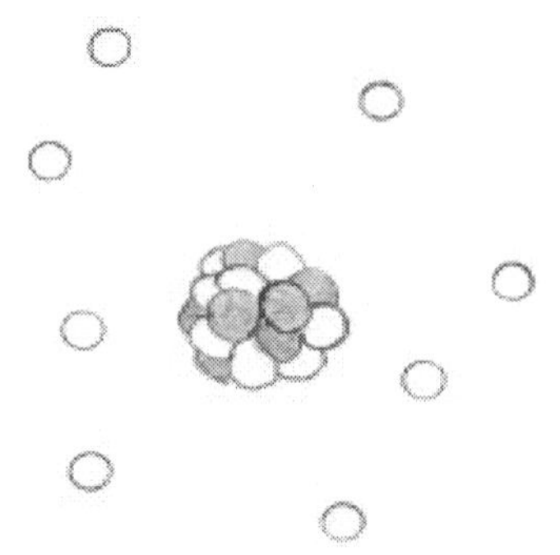

Center nucleus surrounded by electrons
The electrons each have their own orbit around the nucleus

The center nucleus in the drawing consists of both protons (shaded) and neutrons (unshaded). These two give the atom its weight or mass. The outer electrons have a negative charge and balance the positive charge of the protons, but do not provide mass to the atom. Since there are eight electrons, then it would be a good guess that this is oxygen provided that there are also 8 protons. We will cover this more when we reach the periodic table (chart). The neutrons do not have a charge, but have a mass like the protons. The electrons each have their own orbit around the nucleus just like the planets have an orbit around the sun, except that there are several different shaped orbits that we will discuss later.

Element: An element is a substance that cannot be broken down by chemical means. There are currently 118 elements that are known. This is not all the elements in the universe, just those that are known and included in the most up to date periodic table. Ninety one (91) of these are found naturally in nature such as iron, oxygen, and carbon. Elements are defined by the number of protons that they possess and by their atomic weight. An element consists of protons, neutrons and electrons.

Atomic Weight: The atomic weight is the average mass of an atom of that element relative to the mass of carbon, which was assigned a mass of 12. So if carbon weighs 12 grams for its atomic weight, then hydrogen weighs 1 gram. Actually it would be 1.00794 grams. We rounded this off to 1. Chemists think in terms of grams, cc's (cubic centimeters) and liters. You will rarely ever hear of ounces, pounds, or gallons. You will eventually just think in terms of grams, cc's and liters. Grams are weight and cc's and liters are measures of volume. In a laboratory you will use 100 or 250 cc beakers, graduated cylinders, and flasks and measure weight in grams.

Before continuing on with terms and their definitions it would be timely to introduce the Periodic Table of Elements and discuss these. The periodic table that is presented only shows the chemical symbol and its atomic weight, which in most cases has been rounded off to its nearest whole number. After the periodic table of elements is shown, we will show an example of what a more involved element in a more comprehensive table would look like, but for our purposes the Periodic Table shown will answer the problems relative to weights and ideas that are needed for getting started in high school chemistry.

Most periodic tables have the atomic numbers as shown in the atomic number chart following the atomic weight chart. Remember, the atomic number is the number of protons in the atomic nucleus of the atom.

H 1																	He 4
Li 7	Be 9											B 11	C 12	N 14	O 16	F 19	Ne 20
Na 23	Mg 24											Al 27	Si 28	P 31	S 32	Cl 35.5	Ar 40
K 39	Ca 40	Sc 45	Ti 48	V 51	Cr 52	Mn 55	Fe 56	Co 59	Ni 58.6	Cu 63.5	Zn 65	Ga 70	Ge 72.6	As 75	Se 79	Br 80	Kr 84
Rb 85	Sr 87.6	Y 89	Zr 91	Nb 93	Mo 96	Tc 98	Ru 101	Rh 102	Pd 106	Ag 107	Cd 112	In 115	Sn 118	Sb 121	Te 1226	I 127	Xe 131
Cs 132	Ba 137		Hf 178	Ta 180	W 183	Re 186	Os 190	Ir 192	Pt 195	Au 197	Hg 200	Tl 204	Pb 207	Bi 209	Po 209	At 210	Rn 222
Fr 223	Ra 226		Rf 265	Db 268	Sg 271	Bh 270	Hs 277	Mt 276	Ds 281	Rg 280	Cn 285	Uut 284	Fl 289	Uup 288	Lv 293	Uus 294	Uuo 294

La 139	Ce 140	Pr 141	Nd 144	Pm 145	Sm 160	Eu 152	Gd 167	Tb 159	Dy 162.5	Ho 165	Er 167	Tm 169	Yb 173	Lu 175
Ac 227	Th 232	Pa 231	U 238	NP 237	Pu 244	Am 243	Cm 247	Bk 247	Cf 251	Es 252	Fm 257	Md 258	No 259	Lr 262

Periodic Table with symbol and atomic weight

The symbols like H stand for an element. H stands for hydrogen. Those that you most likely will work with in high school chemistry and their representative symbols are:

(Atomic Number and Weight to be filled in by student.)

Symbol	Element	Atomic Number	Atomic Weight
H	Hydrogen		
O	Oxygen		
Na	Sodium		
C	Carbon		
Ca	Calcium		
Cl	Chlorine		
K	Potassium		
Mg	Magnesium		
Ba	Barium		
Ti	Titanium		
Fe	Iron		
Co	Cobalt		

Ni	Nickel
Cu	Copper
Zn	Zink
He	Helium
Al	Aluminum
Si	Silicon
Mn	Manganese
Br	Bromine
Sb	Antimony
Pb	Lead
Hg	Mercury
Cd	Cadmium
P	Phosphorus
Ag	Silver
Au	Gold

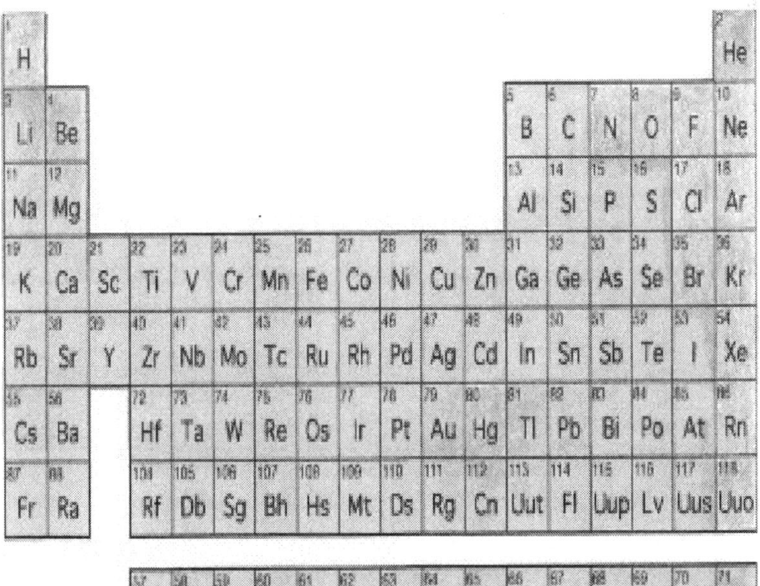

Periodic table with atomic numbers
Atomic numbers 57-71 and 89-103 have been pulled out separately

It would be good to look at the Periodic Table and see if you can locate these elements and note their atomic weights which are written below the element's symbol in the first table. Look at the second Periodic table and notice the number above the symbol displaying the atomic number. Go back to the list of the elements you will most likely work with and write in their atomic weights and atomic numbers as an exercise to familiarize yourself with these. These two charts have been shown separately to emphasize the difference between atomic number and atomic weight.

Most likely there will be a Periodic Table poster on the chemistry room wall in your high school. It may be more elaborate and each element may be represented as follows:

Hydrogen
1
H
1.00794
7 isotopes

The number 1 under the word Hydrogen stands for its atomic number. Under the H is the atomic weight of the element and under that is the number of isotopes that this element can have. The atomic number tells you how many protons in the atom, which is also the number of electrons in that atom. So now let's continue with definitions starting with these new terms;

Atomic Number: An element's atomic number stands for the number of protons or positive charges in its atomic nucleus. It also indicates its position in the periodic table. In a normal element (non-ionized) the number of protons is the same as its electrons. Remember in the definition of an atom we stated that an atom consists of a nucleus of protons and neutrons with electrons that orbit this nucleus. An atom is the smallest component of an element that still retains the chemical properties of that element.

Oxygen
8
O
15.9994
3 isotopes

Oxygen atom

Remember earlier we said that 8 electrons in an atom could be oxygen. Since the oxygen atom has 8 protons, then it has 8 electrons. Since there are 3 isotopes, it may or may not have 8 neutrons. See the explanation under isotopes. Note in the periodic table that we presented earlier the atomic weight of oxygen was rounded to 16. For most work in chemistry oxygen is given the atomic weight of 16 although it is actually 15.9994.

Isotopes: Isotopes are variants of the element. Each of the variants has the same number of protons, but differ in the number of neutrons. For instance carbon 14 is an isotope of carbon 12. They both have 6 protons, but carbon 14 has 8 neutrons, where carbon 12 has 6.

Electrons: Remember that we stated that an atom is made up of three components, the proton, the neutron and the electron. The electrons travel around the proton and neutron nucleus each with a different orbit. The electron has a negative charge and virtually no mass. It is normally equivalent to the number of its protons unless it is an ion in aqueous (water) solution. The electrons are grouped into energy levels and into orbits. Some periodic tables even list the energy levels as follows:

Oxygen	**2**
8	**6**
O	
15.9994	
3 isotopes	

The 2 and the 6 are the electrons in the different energy levels. This will be explained further in class. For now just knowing what the components of a periodic table looks like is a milestone for your first day of class.

Ions: Ions and ion chemistry is the heart of inorganic chemistry. Ions exist in aqueous (water) solutions. An ion is an atom, but it has a different number of electrons than it does protons so that it is no longer in "balance". It now has a charge to it. That charge could be positive or negative. If it is missing an electron, then it has more positive protons than negative electrons and thus it has a positive charge. A positive charged ion is called a **cation**. The charge is based on how many more protons than electrons there are for cations. A negatively charged ion is called an **anion**.

In an aqueous solution (water) if a silver atom of 47 protons only has 46 electrons, then it has a positive charge of plus 1. It would be written Ag^+. On the other hand if an element like chlorine, which has 17 protons has 18 electrons then it would have a negative charge of minus 1 because it has one more electrons than protons and be written Cl^-. A negatively charged ion is called an **anion** as mentioned above.

If a chlorine ion with a minus one charge (Cl^-)shares its extra electron with a silver ion of Ag^+ that is missing an electron, then that forms a precipitate in the water called silver chloride. We will explain this more under the inorganic section. For now just know that ions appear in only aqueous solutions and have to have a charge (either negative or positive) to be an ion. Incidentally, cations retain their elemental names. Sodium is still called sodium as an ion. However, anions become an "ide" when they become ions. Thus chlorine becomes chloride in ion form. Most people have heard of sodium chloride. Incidentally, many salts like sodium chloride do not precipitate or remain solid in water. These are ionic and soluble in water. Thus in water a sodium ion and a chloride atom remain apart in the water as separate ions. Sodium chloride dissolves in water. Chemists say that sodium chloride is soluble in water meaning it dissolves. They do not have a strong ionic bond like AgCl (silver chloride) which does not dissolve in water.

Compound: A compound consists of two or more elements bonded together. It can either be a molecular bond or an ionic bond. For instance, the compound CO mentioned above is made up of carbon and oxygen. It is a gas and as mentioned is called carbon monoxide, which most people know is part of the exhaust of automobiles. This is a molecular bond. Compounds can consist of more than two elements. A compound as well as an individual atom can be ionized. For instance, carbon can have three oxygens to form a carbonate compound that looks like (CO_3) . The three oxygens are bonded to the carbon as a molecular compound. When this compound is in water it can be ionized to form a carbonate ion $(CO_3)^{--}$. Since this carbonate has two extra electrons it could have a partner like Ca^{++} that lacks two electrons. In fact $CaCO_3$ is found in nature and is called calcium carbonate. It is a white solid and only partially ionizes in water. More on this later.

Precipitate: You will spend a great deal of time in inorganic chemistry with ions as mentioned above. When two ions meet in water they may form a precipitate, which is a solid that forms in the water and drops to the bottom of whatever container they are in. For instance, if we mix a clear water solution of sodium carbonate from one vessel and a separate clear solution of calcium chloride from another vessel together in a single vessel like a beaker or test tube, we get a precipitate of calcium carbonate and the ions of sodium and chloride floating freely in this solution. A chemist would write this:

$$Na_2CO_3(aq) + CaCl_2(aq) \rightarrow CaCO_3(s) + 2\ NaCl(aq)$$

Where aq stands for aqueous (water solution) and s stands for solid and $\rightarrow$ means yields the following. In this case the chemist is saying that in water (aq) the Na and CO_3 and the Ca and Cl are ions each with a charge on the left hand side of the equation, but on the right hand side when they all meet together only the Na and Cl are ions because the Ca and CO_3 have formed an ionic bond compound that has solidified or in chemistry terms has formed a precipitate and sunk to the bottom. It would have been more appropriate to write Na^+, Cl^-, Ca^{+2}, and CO_3^{-2-}. However, it is understood that in aqueous form we are talking about charged ions. Some chemists put the charge on, but most assume you know what the charge is in aqueous solution. You will learn rules about solubility and which compounds are soluble and which aren't. For instance, all carbonates (CO_3^{-2}) are insoluble, but all nitrates (NO_3^-) are soluble.

Now you are into the guts of inorganic chemistry. We will explain this more later. For now we are working on the definitions. You will have to know these definitions like they are part of your family if you are going to get that A in chemistry. Read these definitions over and over after you have finished reading and doing the problems. Doing the problems will help in learning the definitions and they will start to sink in the more you read them.

Then when you get to that first day of chemistry, you will be far ahead and able to keep up with the teacher.

Electron orbits and Electron shells: Remember we said that electrons orbit the atomic nucleus (protons and neutrons). Well they do, but there are different orbits. We described the first orbit to be similar to the earth orbiting the sun. In fact that is the first orbit and it is labelled s. Why s, I don't know, but there are all kinds of theories that describe the energy from electrons and how they are positioned around the nucleus.

For now just know that electrons are grouped into orbits around the nucleus. There are quite a number of orbits and each is considered to have a different movement around the nucleus. In addition to the s orbit there is the p orbit, which is like a rubber band that has been squeezed in the middle. Obviously, the more electrons the more orbits. In chemistry the orbits fill in the following sequence 1s, 2s, 2p, 3s, 3p, 4s, 3d, 4p, 5s, 4d, 5p, 6s, 4f, 5d, 6p, 7s, 5f, 6d, 7p, 8s, 5g, 6f, 7d, 8p, and 9s. These designations and theories all evolved over time. The latest one that describes the electrons as I have just shown is called the Quantum Mechanical Model.

If you see something like this ($1s^1$) it simply means that in the first orbit (1s) there is one electron. This is how hydrogen is designated because hydrogen only has one electron to correspond with its one proton. Now helium with atomic number 2 because it has 2 protons is $1s^2$. For a proton like oxygen it is $1s^2 2s^2 2p^4$. Thus oxygen has 8 electrons to correspond to or balance its 8 protons. The electrons in the highest shell are called valence electrons.

Valence: Valence (sometimes called valency) refers to the electrons in the highest occupied energy level of an atom. Valence electrons are the reactive electrons in that they can share with other atoms and are the level that ions obtain their charge.

Valence electrons can be added to subtracted or shared with other atoms. When an element's atoms valence electrons gain more than their proton number then they are negatively charged and have minus for each extra electron. Conversely if they lose an electron so that they have less than the number of protons for that element then they have a positive charge. You may find that there is repetition to some of these definitions explanations. Repetition helps the learning process. Some examples of valence are;

Oxygen -2 written O^{2-} or O^{--}
Sodium +1 written Na^{+}
Carbon can be +2 or +4 so C^{+2} or C^{+4}
Calcium +2 written Ca^{+2} or Ca^{++}
Nitrogen -3,-2,-1,+1, +2, +3, +4,+5
Sulfur -2, +2, +4, + 6

This smattering of definitions will help the student to assimilate this material. Chemistry is considered by most students and teachers to be the hardest and most involved of all the high school subjects. It is thus imperative to listen and take great notes. Now would be a good time to present the best method to truly learn and obtain an A in this subject.

Method and technique to make an A in Chemistry:

1. Get a notebook that is bound. One that you will not lose the pages.
2. Take notes on one side of the page, leaving the other blank. You can take your notes on the right side or the left depending on which is easier for you. I always used the left side.
3. Purchase a good red marking pen.
4. As quickly after class as possible fix your illegible notes. I used to stay in the seat for 5 minutes before running to the next class. I would use my red pen to mark my notes so I could decipher them later on. When you are hurrying to take notes sometimes what seems clear when you are writing cannot be understood when you get home. But it is most likely still fresh in your mind right after class so now you can write over an illegible word

or symbol in red to make it clear for later. If you wait too long you will wonder what the heck you wrote.

5. Before you start any other homework from other subjects copy your chemistry notes from one side of the page to the other. This reinforces what you have learned in class and makes it much neater. By having both pages side by side you can always refer to the original if you copied wrong. I always gave myself a treat when I started doing the copying. When I sat down to do chemistry I had a coke and a candy bar. It was my special time. Now a coke and a candy bar would give me heartburn, but I was younger then. I did the same thing when I took algebra and geometry. If you are taking both math and chemistry, do the math first, then the chemistry.
6. After you have copied your notes, then do your chemistry homework problems. **DO THEM ALL.** Don't be lulled into false security because they seem redundant. Some may be redundant and some may have just a slight trick to them that you would not have caught if you skipped the problem.
7. Check your answers. If you got it wrong, fix it and highlight it in yellow. If you can't figure it out and have struggled with it, then the next day in class the light will shine when your teacher goes over it. But do your best to struggle if necessary to figure it out.
8. Highlight the problems that you missed.
9. Redo the highlighted problems that you missed first time.
10. Write down in red on the problem itself any questions you might have so you can ask them in class.
11. Now you are ready for class.
12. The teacher will likely go over homework and then present new material. If you have done everything above, you will find that it is just refreshing to go over the homework problems that you have already done.
13. Don't get cocky.
14. When you study for your test do practice problems from your homework, especially the ones that were highlighted in yellow. If you miss one, mark it in some way and do it again before the test.

15. This next item can very well make the difference between a B and an A. Many teachers will give students their test back. So if you can find someone from the previous year who still has their tests, get their test and make sure you can do every problem on it. The teacher will not give the same test to you, but knowing how to do the previous year's test is a great way to help know what the teacher considers important. It is a great learning tool. Don't shirk on this one. Find someone who has taken these tests.
16. Smile when your paper comes back with a nice high mark. Because if you follow the above this is what is going to happen.
17. When you do well be prepared for your friends and peers to give you a hard time. Just tell them you find Chemistry fun just like a video game. That should shut them up. Don't let them discourage you or make you feel bad for doing well. Just know that they are jealous and would never admit it. Ten years from now when you have the nice home, the great car and boat, and the great significant other, what they think now will be totally insignificant and meaningless.
18. One last thing–Don't miss one class. You can catch up in history or English, but Chemistry is tough. It's probably 10 times harder than history. If you have to be out sick, try to come in for the Chemistry class and then go back home. Your parents can write you a note. If you are in sports, try to fix your schedule to take Chemistry in the morning so that you are not pulled out at the end of the day for a game or game practice. Some schools like to have special programs where a student leaves class for something. Don't get talked into skipping out on Chemistry.
19. If your teacher is available for help after hours take full advantage of this. For some reason students in high school seem to avoid this teacher help. Maybe you have to ride the bus or his or her times for help are not good, but if the teacher does make time available for help take full advantage of it. You are crazy not to, especially if you want an A.

    Some teachers take email. This is a great way to work with your teacher. Some teachers are great and some aren't. Remember their job is to help you. Don't be bashful about getting help. Also, the internet is a great source of help. If you have a question, type it in in google. Sometimes the internet explains things better than the teacher. However, the teacher should be primary because he or she makes up the test and knows what is important.

Note: When doing homework, some may find that it works better to do it in pieces. Do some now, then take a break, and then come back to it. This is especially true if you hit a wall and can't figure it out. And you will hit walls. Everyone does. It's like going from one level to the next in a video game. When you do hit a wall, take a deep breath and try again or go onto the next problem and then come back to this tough one later. You could also take a break and then come back fresh. Taking a walk around the block is a great break. Or shooting a couple of hoops. Even doing a couple of pushups is good because it puts oxygen in your brain. Whatever works for you is best. The physical activity is good because it negates the coke and candy bar potential weight gain.

So what's the point of all this chemistry stu*ff*?

Well, let's do a problem for example:

Problem: How do you get rid of the carbon dioxide that is produced by power plants in turning coal into energy as well as the exhaust from automobiles? Most of us have heard that we are experiencing global warming due to gases like carbon dioxide being sent into the atmosphere. We have to do something to protect man's future.

Solution: Chemists have been working on this problem and have developed several solutions many of which are in use today. They are also working on additional improved methods.

One method is a chemical scrubber using Calcium Oxide (CaO) as follows:

$CaO + CO_2$ (carbon dioxide) → $CaCO_3$.

$CaCO_3$ is a harmless solid used in many chemical processes such as the making of paper. There is more to it than explained, but you get the general idea. Chemists are working on other methods as well to capture CO_2 and SO_2 (sulfur dioxide) and other harmful gases at the lowest cost. Chemists have "scrubbed" harmful gases and turned them into beneficial compounds used for industry. We are only at the beginning of improving our atmosphere.

There is chemistry in medicine. The chemical composition of DNA, which as everyone knows is the basic building block of life has only recently (last 50 years) been discovered and is still a new science. It is possible that more knowledge of this molecule will lead to the cure and prevention of many diseases. Chemists and biochemists are working on this every day.

Now we are ready to really get into inorganic chemistry.

Inorganic Chemistry:

First, since there is so much to learn, you are going to have to let the teacher guide you. Take those notes and copy them over as soon as possible as we described earlier.

For now a good way to start learning inorganic is to do some simple problems that you should be able to answer based on the definitions that have been given thus far.

Problem 1

What element has the following electron configuration $1s^2 2s^2 2p^6 3s^2 3p^6 3d^{10} 4s^1$?

Solution:

As we stated earlier, the number of electrons is equal to the atomic number. So there are 29 electrons in the above orbits. Since we said that the configuration was the element and not the ion, then the number of electrons must equal the number of protons. Since the number of protons is equal to the atomic number, then all we have to do is go to the periodic chart and find atomic number 29, which turns out to be copper.

29
Copper

Problem 2

What is the valence for the sulfide ion in Calcium Sulfide, written CaS?
Solution:

The sulfide ion can have 4 different valence configurations as described in the definition of valence. However, calcium can only have one configuration and that is Ca^{+2}. Therefore to be in balance, the sulfide ion must be S^{-2}.

Problem 3:

Show the chemical reaction equation when a solution of sodium nitrate and calcium chloride are mixed together. Balance the equation.

Solution:

$Na_2CO_3(aq) + Ca(NO_3)_2(aq) \rightarrow CaCO_3(s) + NaNO_3(aq)$

Okay, now you are really getting into chemistry. First off we know that sodium carbonate has to be two sodium atoms to one carbonate atom. We know this because sodium (Na) has a valence of +1 and the carbonate ion $(CO_3)^{-2}$ has a valence of -2. Thus it takes two sodium atoms to balance one carbonate atom.

It is the same thing with Ca^{+2} and NO_3^-.We know that Calcium is a precipitate and thus we put the (s) to indicate this is a solid. The $NaNO_3$ does not form a precipitate. It's two ions are free to move around in solution. We could have written $NaNO_3$ as Na^+ and NO_3^-, but writing $NaNO_3(aq)$ means two soluble ions.
Now it also said to balance the equation. The number of sodiums and carbonates and calciums and nitrates have to be the same on both sides of the equation. So to balance we have to

work on the right side of the equation. There is one calcium and one carbonate on the left and since there is one calcium and one carbonate on the right then this is okay. But on the left there are two sodiums and two nitrates. Since there are two sodiums and two nitrates on the left there must be two on the right. So we need to put a 2 in front of the $NaNO_3$ to make everything in balance. So the correct balanced equation would be:

$Na_2CO_3(aq) + Ca(NO_3)_2(aq) \rightarrow CaCO_3(s) + 2\ NaNO_3(aq)$

Precipitates and Solubility

A good part of chemistry will be doing equations like problem 3. So to help with this you should memorize the following during your chemistry course. It will help you tremendously in your quest for an A.

1. All nitrates (NO_3^-), chlorates (ClO_3^-) perchlorates (ClO_4^-) and acetates ($Ch_2H_3O_2^-$) are soluble. This means they will always remain in ionic form and not precipitate out with any of the metal ions like Calcium, lead, zinc, iron, etc. The metals are marked on most periodic tables and we will cover that shortly when we go back to the periodic table for more discussion.
2. For now just remember that this is true for all metals except Li^+, Na^+, Rb^+, and Cs^+ ions. They are soluble in water. Thus in the chart below for insoluble anions, when we say all we mean all metals except these 4.

Let's put all this information in a tabular spread sheet form as follows: Remember this chart is not true for ionic compounds of the four cations just mentioned (Li^+, Na^+, Rb^+, and Cs^+)

Soluble Anions	Solubility All or Exceptions
Nitrate (NO3-)	All Nitrates
Chlorate (ClO3-)	All Chlorates
Perchlorate (ClO4-)	All Perchlorates
Acetate (C2H3O2-)	All Acetates
Chloride (Cl^-)	All except Ag, Pb, Hg
Bromide (Br^-)	All except Ag, Pb, Hg

Iodide (I^-)	All except Ag, Pb, Hg
Sulfate (SO4-)	All except Pb, Hg, Ba, Ca, Sr.

Insoluble Anions	**Insolubility All or Exceptions**
Hydroxide (OH-)	All are insoluble
Sulfide (S^{2-})	All are insoluble
Oxide (O^{2-})	All are insoluble
Carbonate (CO_3^{2-})	All are insoluble
Phosphate (PO_4^{3-})	All are insoluble
Oxalate ($C_2O_4^{2-}$)	All are insoluble
Sulfites ((SO3-)	All are insoluble

As mentioned, the anion tabular spread sheet above for insoluble anions is true for all metals except Li^+, Na^+, Rb^+, and Cs^+ ions. All ionized compounds of these dissolve in water into their respective ions and thus are soluble. Also the ammonia compound cation NH_4^+ is soluble in water as well.

Most chemistry books will have a solubility chart that provides how many grams of a substance will dissolve in 100 grams of water. However, you will have to know most of the precipitates commonly used in chemistry tests. A good exercise would be to take this information on solubility and list all the precipitates. Then memorize this. It will be invaluable to you. To get you started, here is a partial list of common precipitates found in chemistry and on chemistry tests:

$CaCO_3$
$Ca(OH)_2$
$BaSO_4$
PbS
$SrSO_4$
AgCl
$SrCO_3$

Etc.

Problem 4:

Show the chemical reaction equation when a solution of strontium nitrate and a solution of potassium carbonate are mixed together. Balance the equation.

Solution:

Let's just write it out just the way the question is asked:

$Sr(NO_3)_2 + K_2CO_3 \rightarrow$?

Anytime you are unsure of the charge on an ion you can go to Google and write the name of the ion in the search window and it will take you to several sites that will tell you the charge. Just put in strontium ion and see what happens. You could also put in "charge of strontium ion" and that would work as well. It will quickly tell you that it is Sr^{+2}. Since from the information already given you would know that NO_3 has a single minus charge, then you know it takes two nitrate ions to balance the strontium and thus strontium nitrate is written $Sr(NO_3)_2$. It is the same with potassium carbonate (K_2CO_3)

So from the information already given, we know that strontium carbonate is a precipitate and thus the reaction would look like this before balancing and after balancing:

$Sr(NO_3)_2 + K_2CO_3 \rightarrow SrCO_3 + KNO_3$ **unbalanced**

$Sr(NO_3)_2 + K_2CO_3 \rightarrow SrCO_3 + 2\ KNO_3$ **balanced**

We could have shown $SrCO_3$ as $SrCO_3(s)$ to indicate it is a precipitate, but most of the time chemists do not do this. Your chemistry book may or may not use the (s and aq). My recommendation would be to put the s and aq designations in.

Other very serious reasons for doing well in Chemistry are:

1. Better paying career job out of high school.

2. For those going to college, it will provide opportunity for serious scholarship money. See the attached article from my local Birmingham paper about scholarships. The attached news article shows the amount for grade average and ACT scores (college entrance tests). For an ACT of 30 and a score of B+ in high school, the scholarship pays $ 9,000 per year. Even a B average qualifies. With a B and an ACT of 24 you get $3,500 per year according to the article. You have to be an Alabama resident or live in certain counties in Florida and Mississippi to qualify. Most every state has similar programs for residents of their state.
3. Doing well in Chemistry will help you if you go on to take Physics. It also enhances your skill in math.
4. Doing well in Chemistry and then the other math and sciences will open up doors in many fields like lab technicians, industrial chemists, pharmacists, medicine (from technicians to doctors), engineering, computer programming, technicians in all fields, technical maintenance of high tech equipment, technical sales, and much more.
5. Getting into two year technical schools. Technical schools enable their graduates to go right into high tech jobs that pay well and are extremely interesting. Industry is crying for these graduates and paying to get them. Many industries will provide tuition assistance to their employees to go to these schools. The key is to do well in science and math now.
6. Chemistry teaches you about reasoning and logical thinking and improves your concept of the world. It allows you to improve your mental muscles just like an athlete must work his physical muscles to compete in the world.
7. Most important it provides you with the understanding of the world around you. You will look at things differently and you will have opened up a whole new world and potential for a wonderful life.

High-Quality Academic Programs and Great Scholarships for Birmingham Area Students!

NEW!

The University of South Alabama is pleased to increase academic scholarships for resident and non-resident students through the new

MITCHELL-MOULTON SCHOLARSHIP INITIATIVE

Available for 2014 High School Graduates. Apply today!

These are the scholarships listed from the University of South Alabama for Alabama residents plus Mississippi students from George, Greene, Harrison, Jackson, Perry and Stone Counties and Florida students from Escambia and Santa Rosa counties.

ACT Composite Score	SAT Equivalent (SAT Critical Reading + Math)	Minimum High School GPA	Annual Amount	4 Year Total Amount
33 or higher	1440 or higher	3.5	$11,000	$44,000
32	1400-1430	3.5	$9,000	$36,000
30-31	1330-1390	3.5	$8,000	$32,000
28-29	1250-1320	3.5	$5,000	$20,000
24-27	1090-1240	3.0	$3,500	$14,000
23	1050-1080	3.0	$2,500	$10,000

ACT Composite Score	SAT Equivalent (SAT Critical Reading + Math)	Minimum High School GPA	Annual Amount	4 Year Total Amount
33 or higher	1440 or higher	3.5	$12,000	$48,000

32	**1400-1430**	**3.5**	**$10,000**	**$40,000**
30-31	**1330-1390**	**3.5**	**$9,000**	**$36,000**
28-29	**1250-1320**	**3.5**	**$6,500**	**$26,000**
27	**1210-1240**	**3.5**	**$5,000**	**$20,000**

***Back to inorganic chemistry*:**

***Acid and Base*:**

Everyone knows that acid like sulfuric acid can eat through many things. It is used to clean brick. It is used to etch glass. It is known to cause severe burns if it gets on the skin.

So what is acid chemically? Well it is an excess of hydrogen ions in an aqueous (water) solution. The more H^+ ions in the water the more acidic it is and the more dangerous. That's it. It's not complicated. The measure of the strength of an acid is called pH. The lower the number of pH the stronger the acid is. It would seem like it should be the other way around, but it's not. Lower is stronger. Thus pH 1 will eat your skin off. Stomach acid is pH 3. Looking at the numbers one would wonder why your stomach doesn't disintegrate. First of all there is a major increase going from pH 3 to 2, like 10 times more powerful. Most food is in the pH 4 to pH 6 range. So this is relatively mild. However, pH of 4 can give one heartburn. Again this is because there is a major difference between a pH of 4 and 5. From pH 3 to 5 is a 100 times difference (10X10). Stomach acid is hydrochloric acid, which by now you should know chemically looks like HCl. In water it is totally soluble and forms H^+ and Cl^-.

Some of you may have heard that pure water is a pH of 7. These numbers were picked arbitrarily years ago. Well actually pH is the negative log of hydrogen ion concentration in an aqueous (water) solution. The p means power (potenz in German) and thus pH is the power of hydrogen ions. From one number to the next it is a factor of 10 times more powerful.

Above pH of 7 the hydrogen ions are gone and replaced by basic or alkaline ions. These alkaline ions are OH^- ions. OH^- ions are called hydroxyl ions. A solution of these ions have a slick feel. This is why water with a pH above 7 is called soft water because the more basic or alkaline the slicker or softer to the feel. The most commonly known alkaline solution is sodium hydroxide, NaOH. NaOH can go as high as 14 pH depending on the concentration or grams of sodium hydroxide to grams of water. Other alkaline solutions are KOH and LiOH. Don't be fooled by the comment that alkaline feels soft. It too can eat skin off.

What happens if you mix HCl and NaOH. I would not advise it especially in concentrated form. It is a violent reaction at high concentrations and bubbles forth hydrogen gas. At low concentrations it would simply be used to neutralize the water. If a pH of 9 NaOH and pH of 5 HCl were mixed the end result would be plain water. But if you mixed a pH of 1 and a pH of 14 it would be violent and boil off the water and release hydrogen gas.

The reaction whether it is low concentrated solutions or high concentration of solutions of HCl and NaOH would be:

$$HCl + NaOH \rightarrow H_2O + NaCl$$

However, as mentioned if he pH differential is large the reaction would cause the H^+ to reduce to elemental hydrogen gas ($H^{2)}$ and since it is an exothermic (gets hot) reaction it boils the water.

Any time there is an $H^+ + OH^-$ ion in the same solution they will immediately grab onto each other and form water.

Problem 5:

What happens if you mix a solution of Barium Hydroxide and Hydrochloric acid? Write and balance the equation.

Write the question in equation form first:

$$Ba(OH)_2 + HCL \rightarrow ?$$

Then solve it:

$$Ba(OH)_2(s) + HCL(aq) \rightarrow H_2O(aq) + BaCl_2(aq) \text{ unbalanced}$$

$$Ba(OH)_2(s) + 2\ HCL(aq) \rightarrow 2\ H_2O(aq) + BaCl_2(aq) \text{ balanced}$$

This may not look right until you understand the following:

$H^+ + OH^- \rightarrow HOH$ which is H_2O

In this case you have two OH^- ions from the $Ba(OH)_2$
And two H^+ ions from the 2 HCl ions

Note: You mixed a solid and a liquid and obtained all liquid.

Before you finish the course in chemistry this will be second nature. If you read this book on chemistry and apply the method discussed you will have a major head start towards an A in this course. It will be like having a 10 minute head start in a 5k race.

Problem 6:

What happens if you mix a solution of Barium Hydroxide and Sulfuric acid? Write and balance the equation.

Solution: Write the question in equation form first:

$$Ba(OH)_2 + H_2SO_4 \rightarrow ?$$

Then solve it:

$$Ba(OH)_2 + H_2SO_4 \rightarrow H_2O + BaSO_4 \text{ unbalanced}$$

$$Ba(OH)_2 + H_2SO_4 \rightarrow 2\ H_2O + BaSO_4 \text{ balanced}$$

Revisiting the Periodic Chart

3 Li	4 Be																
11 Na	12 Mg											13 Al					
19 K	20 Ca	21 Sc	22 Ti	23 V	24 Cr	25 Mn	26 Fe	27 Co	28 Ni	29 Cu	30 Zn	31 Ga					
37 Rb	38 Sr	39 Y	40 Zr	41 Nb	42 Mo	43 Tc	44 Ru	45 Rh	46 Pd	47 Ag	48 Cd	49 In	50 Sn				
55 Cs	56 Ba	71 Lu	72 Hf	73 Ta	74 W	75 Re	76 Os	77 Ir	78 Pt	79 Au	80 Hg	81 Tl	82 Pb	83 Bi	84 Po		
87 Fr	88 Ra	103 Lr	104 Rf	105 Db	106 Sg	107 Bh	108 Hs	109 Mt	110 Ds	111 Uuu	112 Uub						

Periodic Chart with only Metals (Cations)
(Numbers stand for atomic number)

All of the metals in the periodic chart are listed. These are all cations with a positive charge. Only the metals have a positive charge. There is one additional cation besides these metals. It is a polyatomic ion. It is NH_4^+ the ion of ammonia. All other polyatomic atoms that are ionized are negatively charged like CO_3^{-2}.

The reason the first column is shaded is because these are the only metal elements whose ions are **always** soluble. These elements are called the alkali metals. We already know that NaOH is extremely alkaline. All the alkali metals are extremely alkaline. You will learn more about the groupings of the periodic chart, but for now just know that these metals that are shaded are the elements whose ions are soluble in water and are called the alkali metals. They do not precipitate out like say $CaCO_3$. Na_2CO_3 is soluble in water. These alkali metals also have a charge of +1. There are other metals with a charge of +1 like Ag^+. Some metal ions have the capability of having two different charges like copper (Cu). It can either be Cu^+ or Cu^{+2}.

This means you could have either CuCl or $CuCl_2$ for example. None of the alkali group have this capability. Their charge is always plus 1. Most of the metals just have the capability of one charge and it is usually plus one or plus two.

Don't worry if this seems a bit confusing at this point. It's new to you, but you will be surprised at how much this is going to aid you when you start taking the course. Read this several times and do the problems. You can learn a great deal from the problems. The main thing is that this studying now will avoid your being overwhelmed when you start the course. It will come together. The more you look at this material the more it will sink in. And remember to get the most out of what the teacher is saying by sitting up front if you can and taking notes in class using the method outlined earlier in the chapter.

As a reminder, the numbers in the chart are the atomic number, which you know is the number of protons in the nucleus of the atom. Repetition is good. You probably remember this number also is the number of electrons.

Molarity and Molality:

For some reason this is a hard concept for students to grasp and it is the one that usually hurts a student's grade. If you can grasp this concept, you will do fine in chemistry assuming you work at it. Here goes:

Molarity (M) is defined as the number of moles of solute dissolved in one liter of solution.

Given formula- Molarity (M) = moles of solute/liter of solution

Right off the bat, you are probably saying—"What the heck does that mean? What's a mole and what's a solute? And while you're at it, what's a liter really.

In chemistry, a mole is not a furry creature that boroughs underground. A chemical mole is really the atomic weight of the solute. Now what is the solute. Well in this case it is the substance that you are putting in the water that dissolves in the water or any solution or solvent. It can be NaCl or it can be antifreeze as long as it dissolves in the water or any solution. It can be the amount of oil in gasoline.

You have to have the combined solute and receiving material be one liter to state the amount in the one liter total. Okay a liter is a volumetric measurement just like gallons. In fact one liter is equal to .264 gallons. So it is closer to a quart. I hesitate telling you this because you need to think in terms of liters and not think about converting it to what you are familiar with.

In chemistry lab you may see a glass liter beaker that you should use as your reference point to what a liter looks like. It will likely be the biggest beaker you will see. You will also see a glass cylinder for measuring milliliters. This cylinder is usually 100 milliliters or mL. Picture a glass cylinder about ten inches high and about an inch and one half in diameter. This is what you will eventually see in lab and it is 100 mL. Ten of these cylinders would equal one liter because there are 1,000 mL. in a liter. Try to picture these ten cylinders now and call it a liter.

So a mole is the amount of equivalent atomic weight amount of something that you put in a one liter beaker or anything that holds a liter. Let's just do one for example that is simple. Let's put one mole of sodium chloride into that one liter beaker that is not quite full of water. Then we will bring the level of the cylinder to the one liter mark so that the salt (NaCl) and water will together equal one liter. A single mole of NaCl weighs approximately as follows:

$$\begin{aligned} Na &= 23 \text{ grams} \\ Cl &= \underline{35.5} \text{ grams} \\ Total &= 58.5 \text{ grams} \end{aligned}$$

We got this from the first periodic chart we showed. So a one molar solution of NaCl would be 58.5 grams of NaCl in a solution of one liter of combined NaCl and water. Not so hard really.

Problem 7:

How many moles are in a 100 mL solution of potassium chloride if the potassium chloride that was put in the solution weighed 3 grams?

Solution:

There are two ways to mathematically do this. First way will explain it and the second way will be more of a check, but use whatever method you are most comfortable with.

Method 1:

First, put the problem question in terms of an equation:

Moles (Molarity) = moles of KCl/liter of solution

Now we need to find the moles of KCL in 3 grams
Since one mole of KCl equals 39 g (K) + 35.5 g (Cl) = 74.5 g (grams KCl) then,

3/74.5 = .04 Moles if it were in one liter of water and KCl.

Since this is in 100 ml. we now need to convert to one liter

Since one liter is equal to 1,000 ml. then we need to multiply by 10

10 x .04 = .4 Moles or Molarity

Method 2: Some students may like this better

Solution Concentration in M/L =

$$\frac{3\ \mathbf{g\ KCL}}{100\ \mathbf{mL}} \times \frac{1\ \text{mol KCl}}{74.5\ \mathbf{g\ KCl}} \times \frac{1{,}000\ \mathbf{mL}}{1\ \text{L}}$$

Go ahead and cross out the darkened g KCl and the darkened mL leaving just the mol KCl per 1 L.

Doing the math (3 x 1,000)/(100 x 74.5) = .4 Moles or Molarity

Obviously, either method is fine and they are a good check for each other. Now for **molality.** Its similar but not the same as molarity. Just make sure on a test that you have your eyes sharp to see the difference.

Molality (m) is defined as the number of moles of solute dissolved in one kilogram of solvent.

Molality (m) = moles of solute/kilogram of solvent

Note the small m for molality as opposed to the big M for molarity. It's enough to make us realize our immortality. Sorry for the lame joke, just wanted to make sure you were awake.

Note: We have not told you yet, but there are 1,000 grams in one kilogram. I'm not going to tell you the relationship to pounds because you need to start thinking in terms of grams and kilograms. Sufficient for now is to tell you that an average textbook weighs one kilogram. This is what I want you to picture. Thus if it were around a 900 page book factoring in the weight of the cover assuming it weighed around 100 pages, then one gram would be around the weight of one page of the book. If you look on a food label and it says there are two grams of fat in one serving, then you would be eating about two pages worth of fat.

Problem 8:

How many grams of sodium iodide (NaI) must be dissolved in 500 grams of water to make a 0.2 molal NaI solution?

Solution:

Writing the question into formula:

Molarity (m) = moles of solute/kg of solvent

$$\textbf{kg } \mathbf{H_2O} \times \frac{\textbf{mol solute}}{1.0 \textbf{ kg } \mathbf{H_2O}} \times \frac{\text{g solute}}{\textbf{1 mol solute}} = \text{g of solute}$$

Na = 23 grams
I = 127 grams
150 grams

0.2 x 150 = 30 grams of NaI in 1 mol NaI

Since it is only 500 grams or half of 1 kg

Then only **15 grams** are needed for this solution

(if you need 30 grams for 1,000 kg then you only need 15 for 500 to keep the same ratio)

Or you could have done it in equation format:

$$0.5\ \mathbf{kg\ H_2O} \times \frac{0.2\ \mathbf{mol\ NaI}}{1.0\ \mathbf{Kg\ H_2O}} \times \frac{150\ \text{g NaI}}{\mathbf{1\ mol}\ \text{NaI}} = 15\ \text{g NaI}$$

the darkened items cross out leaving grams of NaI

States of Matter

Substances exist in one of three states, solid, liquid, and/or gas. These three states are reversible. By adding heat you can change the state of ice to water and then to gas (steam). You can reverse the process by "cooling it down" by removing heat energy.

If you put an ice cube in a pot on the stove and applied heat, it would soon melt into water. As you melt the ice there is both water and ice together for some period until all the ice is dissolved. If you had a thermometer in the pot, the temperature of the water and ice would remain at 32 degrees Fahrenheit or 100 degrees Centigrade. The heat going into the mixture of ice and water is strictly going into the ice to change its state. Then after the ice is gone, the heat going into the pot is used up raising the temperature until the temperature reaches boiling point 212° Fahrenheit or 100° Centigrade. Then again the energy goes into changing the state until all the water is turned into steam (gas).

The concept that will be taught in chemistry is that there is a different level of heat required to change state than is used to raise the temperature. The other concept that will be taught is that to change the water back to ice requires the same amount of energy. But this time you are removing heat. The same amount of heat to melt the ice is the same as that to "freeze it". Only in going from ice to water you are putting heat in and in going from water to ice you are removing heat.

It all has to do with the kinetic energy of the molecules. The more energy applied the greater the energy of the molecule. The greater the energy the more the molecule will tend to expand its space by travelling faster and harder. Adding heat can cause a liquid to become a gas and as heat is continued to be added the molecules expand even more. In a closed container the molecules cannot expand beyond the limits of the container and thus exert added pressure on the container walls. The walls may even bulge because of the added pressure. Thus heat, pressure and volume are all related. There are several laws and equations that you will learn in chemistry (more so in physics) covering the relationship of temperature, pressure, and volume. We will let the teacher cover these. For now we just wanted to cover the concept. You will actually get more of this in physics. One thing you will always see on tests is the conversion of Centigrade and Fahrenheit. They are just two different measurements of temperature. Chemists use Centigrade more than Fahrenheit.

Changing Fahrenheit into Centigrade and vice versa:

The formulas for changing one temperature to the other are:

$$F = 9/5 \times 100C + 32$$

And

$$C = 5/9(F - 32)$$

Problem 9:

If it is 100 degrees Centigrade what is the temperature in Fahrenheit?

Solution: Use the formula $F = 9/5\ C + 32$

$$F = 9/5 \times 100 + 32$$

$$F = 180 + 32$$

$$F = 212 \text{ degrees Fahrenheit}$$

You will see this on tests in chemistry. It is on most every final exam and probably on many ACT college entrance exams.

Problem 10:

If it is 100 degrees Centigrade what is the temperature in Fahrenheit?

$$C = 5/9(212 - 32)$$

Do the operation inside the parenthesis first

$$C = 5/9(180)$$

C = 100 degrees Centigrade

More about Ions:

By now you have a good idea of the relationship of elements, atoms, and ions. Your teacher may demonstrate some characteristics of ions. For instance she may put distilled water into a beaker. Pure distilled water is free of ions. She may attach a metal probe onto each side of the beaker and run a wire to one end of the probe and connect the other end to a battery. Then she may attach the other end of the battery to a light and the other end of the light to the other electrode in the beaker. An electrode is just a metal rod sort of like a good sized steel nail. The pictorial below shows the circuit.

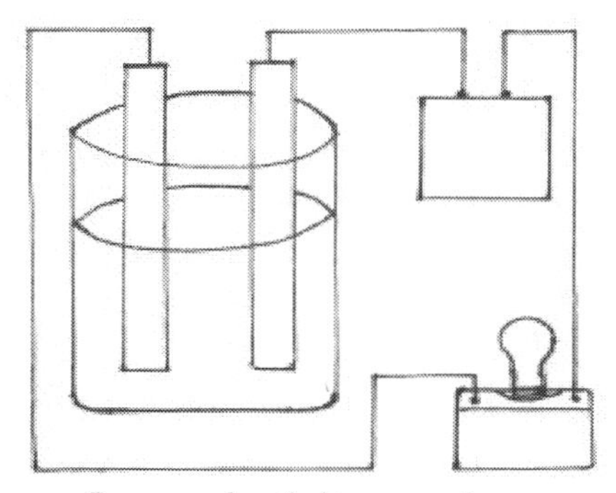

Ion conductivity experiment

When the battery is connected nothing happens. However, when everyday table salt (NaCl) is added to the water the light begins to glow. The more salt the brighter the light. The reason for this is because the positive and negative ions act as a conductor of electricity. However, there is more because over time the plus ions of Na line up on one side and the minus ions of chlorine line up on the other side and a new reaction occurs that actually emits chlorine gas and hydrogen gas. You probably won't go this far in chemistry because the experiment won't last that long. The experiment demonstrated that ions conduct in water.

It is important to know that the ionized material in this case NaCl (table salt) is called an electrolyte. All ionized liquids are called electrolytes. You will study more about electrolytes in chemistry. One of the uses of electrolytes is batteries. Let's talk next about batteries and how ions carrying electricity can become a battery by the correct use of specific electrodes and having the correct electrolyte.

Batteries and oxidation-reduction reactions:

Now if you took two beakers like the ones in the drawing and put an electrode made of zinc metal in one beaker and an electrode made of copper in the other you have the beginning of a crude battery. You next have to have a liquid bridge so that ions can flow back and forth between beakers. This is accomplished with an inverted U shaped glass tube as seen in the drawing.

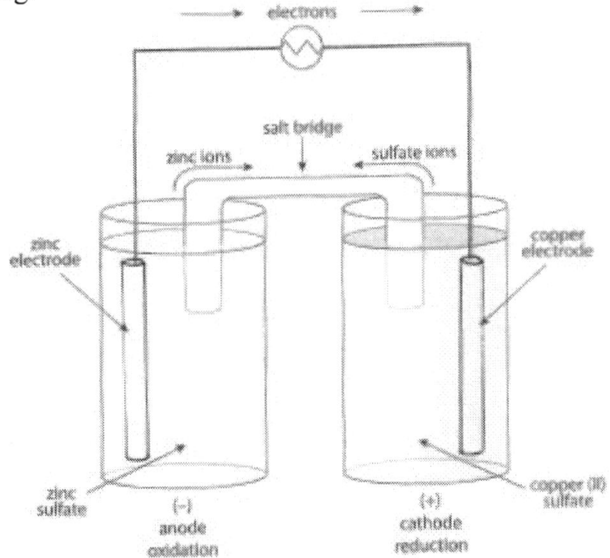

Galvanic cell creating a current from an electrolyte
(Drawing obtained from Wikipedia[8])

[8] Source is Wikipedia's own work and the author is listed as Hazmat2. January 4, 2012. Drawing downloaded on February 6, 2014.

The two electrodes are shown with electrons traveling across the wires going through a device for measuring electrical volts (voltmeter). If an appropriate light bulb were connected instead of the voltmeter like in the previous drawing then it too would light.

There are two electrolytes (ion solutions) that are used in this Galvanic cell battery. These are zinc sulfate ($ZnSO_4$) and copper sulfate ($CuSO_4$). This same methodology is used in car batteries only with different electrodes and using H_2SO_4 (sulfuric acid) as the electrolyte.

Okay so how do batteries like the Galvanic cell work? Well they work through two chemical reactions that are going on in this battery. One is called an oxidation reaction and the other is called a reduction reaction.

Oxidation reaction:

An oxidation reaction occurs when an element loses electrons. It therefore develops a plus charge. Metals oxidize when oxygen causes the metal to "rust" by giving up its electrons to an oxygen molecule. In the case of the Galvanic cell the following reaction occurs at the zinc electrode:

$$Zn^{o} \text{ (solid)} \rightarrow Zn^{2+} + 2\ e^{-} \text{ (electrons)}$$

At the same time that this oxidation is occurring in the beaker on the left, there is a reduction reaction occurring in the beaker on the right.

Reduction reaction:

A reduction reaction occurs when an element gains an electron. In the case above, the copper ions in solution (Cu^{++}) now become reduced back to their metal state and plate out on the copper electrode. The reaction is as follows:

$$Cu^{2+} + 2\ e^{-} \rightarrow Cu^{o}$$

Now both reactions are occurring simultaneously for this to work. The bridge allows the ions to travel back and forth as shown in the drawing. The purpose of the bridge is to maintain a charge balance.

If you add the two reactions together and you must because they cannot happen unless they are both operating then you get the following reaction:

$$Zn^{o} \text{ (solid)} + Cu^{2+} + \mathbf{2\ e^{-}} \rightarrow Zn^{2+} + \mathbf{2\ e^{-}} + Cu^{o}$$

The electrons cancel out because they flow through the wire creating an electric current and therefore cancel out in the equation. The electric current would be used up either by lighting the bulb or getting the wires "hot". The equation would be written without showing the electrons, but for purposes of clarity for the student they were left in.

The interesting thing about a car battery is that the alternator creates an electric current through the battery thus reversing the reaction. The plated material like the copper in the Galvanic cell is then oxidized back to its ion form and the ionized element like Cu^{2+} is then plated back to the electrode. In theory a car battery should last forever. Chemists and metallurgists are working to make batteries last longer and longer. The electrodes decay over time even though they are renewed chemically.

These same oxidation and reduction type reactions are used to plate metals onto other metals. Gold and silver are plated onto copper using this same technique.

This is just the tip of the iceberg in the wonderful world of chemistry. This short course in inorganic chemistry has hit the highlights and given you an overview that will give you the basics to make that A in the course, assuming you follow the method discussed earlier or a modified version of your own[9].

Laboratory Work:

Laboratory exercises vary from school to school. Just make sure that you get the point of the lab and don't get too involved

---

[9] The method I described of taking notes is to me the best methodology, but I know that students may have one that they feel more comfortable with. The key is to review these notes as soon after they are taken and to be sure that they are legible so you don't have to scratch your head when you get home at night. I highly recommend my method, but if you have something better fine. If not use mine.

in the mechanics such that the purpose eludes you. Things don't always work properly in lab. Show the teacher that you are doing your best and **ask him or her for help right away if it is not going correctly.** And above all follow the safety rules that the teacher gives you. Chemistry can be very dangerous. There are many accidents reported every year form explosions to burns in high school labs.

The key is to know what the purpose of the experiment was. If you don't get it, ask the teacher after it is over what the experiment was supposed to teach you. Don't be embarrassed to ask.

Now let's switch from inorganic chemistry to organic chemistry. You are going to have to be good in both of these to get that A.

Organic Chemistry:

If you look at a typical chemistry book, the subject of organic chemistry covers at best one third of the book and is usually at the end. Don't be fooled by this. Organic chemistry is far more involved than this would lead you to believe. For one thing there are by far more organic compounds than inorganic. There are over a million organic compounds known, which is way more than the inorganic. Organic chemicals are developed daily for medicines, cosmetics, paints, fuels, industrial solvents, soaps, toothpastes, food additives and supplements, feeds and food substitutes, colorants, batteries, clothing, housing, toys, plastics of every kind and much more.

It would be wise to familiarize yourself with organic chemistry now and review it again when you come to the end of the inorganic teaching in your high school. The organic session usually comes at the end of the third quarter of the year when time is precious because you are nearing final exams. There is a tremendous amount of memorizing in organic so it would be wise to start memorizing before it starts. I will give you the information to memorize for starters.

The inventions of organic plastics like nylon, rayon, polyester, Styrofoam, Teflon, synthetic rubber, polystyrene, polypropylene, and Lexan (bullet proof glass) are so recent that there are people alive today that were born before these were invented. So in the scheme of things we are still in the era of chemistry innovations. DNA was discovered when I was in college. I believe we are just at the beginning of what DNA research chemists and biochemists will do to improve human health.

So what is Organic Chemistry?

Organic chemistry is defined as the study of all chemicals containing carbon. There are only a very few exceptions where a substance containing carbon is considered inorganic. These are calcium carbide (CaC_2), metal carbonates like sodium (Na_2CO_3,) copper, and calcium carbonate, and oxides of carbon like CO and CO_2.

Each organic carbon has 4 electrons in its outer shell giving it the ability to bond to 4 single bond atoms with one extra electron each or it can use two of its 4 vacancies to bond to atoms with two extra electrons. Most of the time there will usually be at least one hydrogen ion bound to the carbon thus giving the name hydrocarbons to organic chemistry compounds. Two good examples are methane and ethane.

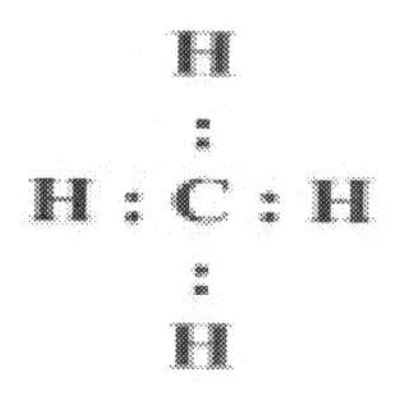

Methane

Methane is the simplest known organic compound. The first thing you must know is that these compounds are not ionic compounds. They are covalent compounds. Covalent because they "co share" the valence electrons. Remember we said there were two types of compounds, ionic and covalent. The difference is that ionic share electrons and so a Ca^{2+} ion is looking for an ion with two extra electrons so it can bond.

Covalent bonding is nothing like that. In covalent bonding the atoms have the same number of protons that they do electrons and thus they do not have a charge What they do is pair up to form a covalent bond. Covalent bonds are extremely strong bonds. In the case of carbon there are 4 electrons in its outer shell and hydrogen has one electron. Carbon can therefore connect these 4 electrons to anything it wants. It can be to four hydrogen atoms that each have one electron as in the methane molecule above.

In the case of Ethane, there are two carbon atoms as shown in the illustration for Ethane as follows:

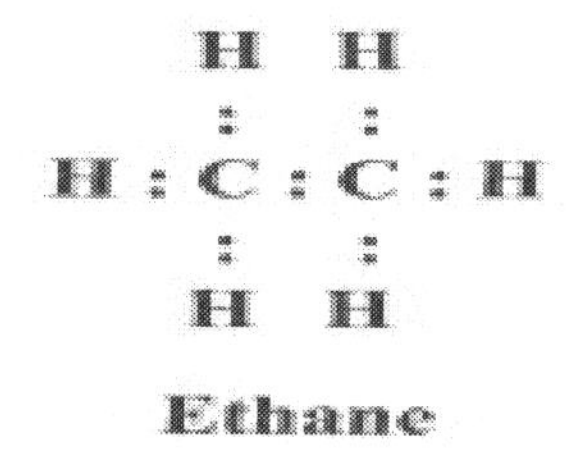

Ethane

Thus the covalent bonding is still satisfied, but each carbon shares one of its electrons with one of the electrons of another carbon. Just remember that each carbon can attach to four positions. The reason I say positions is because sometimes you will have an atom that covalently bonds with carbon that has two covalent bonding positions in its electron shell. Oxygen is a good example. It has two covalent bonding positions.

Let's illustrate, but first instead of continuing to use the dots, chemists use straight lines in place of the dots to designate the bonding. In fact they just write the elements without showing the bonding with the expectation that you can tell what the bonding is. After a few days of class you will be expected to do this as well.

So first let's do it in two steps so you see what I mean. First step will be to use the lines in place of dots and replace two of the hydrogens in ethane with one oxygen as follows:

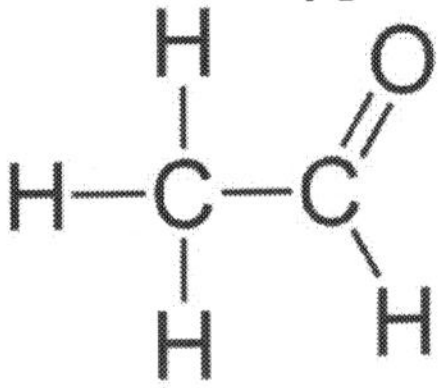

Ethyl aldehyde also written CH_3CHO

Ethyl aldehyde is also called acetaldehyde and ethanal. Note the carbon is still showing 4 bonds. This is important to remember. Carbon always covalent bonds in four places. Most of the time these chemicals will be written like CH_3CHO without showing the bonds. You are just expected to know that the first carbon has three covalent hydrogen bonds and one carbon bond. The second carbon has a double bonded oxygen, a hydrogen atom and it is bonded to the first carbon as well.

Organic chemistry is a great deal of memorizing in high school chemistry. You will have to know how to name the different classifications of organic chemicals and how they react. I will give you the classifications and naming conventions. This will give you a major head start when you get to this part of organic chemistry. I majored in chemistry in college and took advanced courses. You just have to memorize these things to go on and do the fun things in chemistry like develop new compounds, which was part of my advanced course years ago. If you work in industrial chemistry like I did all this becomes very important.

Hydrocarbons:

Hydrocarbons are all organic compounds that have nothing but carbon and hydrogen in them. Both methane and ethane fit the bill. However, obviously acetaldehyde does not fit the classification.

Alkanes:

Alkanes are defined as hydrocarbons with only single covalent bonds. An alkane is a single bonded carbon to carbon chain with only hydrogens to full the other bonds. The carbon chain can be a straight chain or it can be branched. Both methane and ethane are alkanes. Let's add a carbon to ethane to make propane.

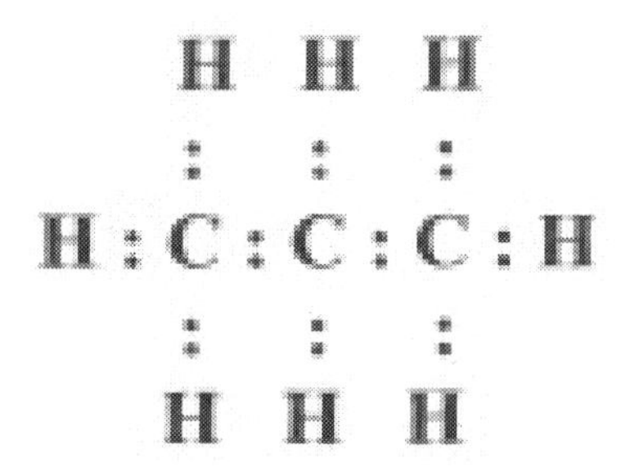

Propane- a 3 carbon alkane

The alkane in the illustration is propane. It has three carbons and all single bonds and only carbon and hydrogen. Now we said that you could replace the two dots (single bond) with a line or you could just write it out as $CH_3CH_2CH_3$. Chemists most often write it this way. But then what happens as you add more carbons. Say you have a total of ten carbons. A ten carbon alkane is called decane.

That's a lot to write out so chemists then decided that they would write decane as $CH_3(CH_2)_8CH_3$. Draw your own decane carbon chain and you will see that the (CH_2) just repeats itself 8 times. The CH_2 group is called an ethyl group and the CH_3 is called a methyl group. So anything after propane is written as $CH_3(CH_2)_nCH_3$ where n equals two less than the total number of carbons. So a six carbon chain, which is called hexane would be $CH_3(CH_2)_4CH_3$.

In fact the first 10 alkanes are methane, ethane, propane, butane, pentane, hexane, heptane, octane, nonane, and decane. Obviously, some of these names are familiar to you. You may use propane gas or a butane gas lighter. All this is straight forward, it just needs to be remembered for tests. That's why I say there is a good deal of memorization required for organic chemistry.

Now we said that alkanes can have branches. Let's do one.

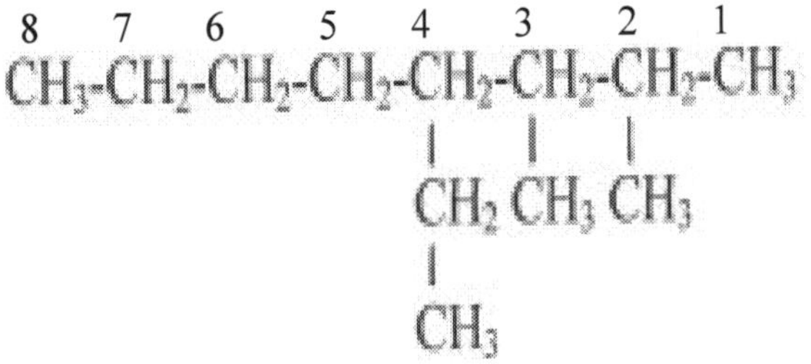

```
 8     7     6     5     4     3     2     1
CH3-CH2-CH2-CH2-CH2-CH2-CH2-CH3
                        |     |     |
                       CH2   CH3   CH3
                        |
                       CH3
```

4-ethyl-2,3-dimethyl octane

The name of this alkane is 4-ethyl-2,3, dimethyl octane. The way these are named is as follows:

1. First you look for the longest chain. It doesn't have to be horizontal, it can be vertical. It is smart to flip it horizontal so the longest chain is up top and horizontal like the illustration for ease of putting the name to it.
2. Then you look for the closest branch to an end. The end that is closest to the branch becomes number one carbon and then you number down the chain. Had the closest chain been where the 7 is, then this would have been two and the numbers would have gone from one to eight left to right.
3. Now you need to know that CH_3 is called a methyl group. CH_2 is called an ethyl group. Just in case you forgot.
4. Since there are two methyl groups, there is going to be a dimethyl in the name. The rest is easy. You just put it together as 4-ethyl-2,3, dimethyl octane.

In case you were wondering what other hydrocarbons exist besides alkane, here are three. Remember that we said that alkanes can only have single bonds. Well single bond hydrocarbons have all the hydrogens filling the carbon positions available. This is called a saturated hydrocarbon. But if you remove two hydrogens somewhere so that two adjacent carbons have one hydrogen each, then this compound has to have a double bond between these two carbons. When a double bond exists then we say the molecule is unsaturated.

$$CH_3\text{-}CH_2\text{-}CH{=}CH\text{-}CH_2\text{-}CH_2\text{-}CH_2\text{-}CH_3$$

A double bond in a hydrocarbon

A hydrocarbon with a double bond is called an alkene. If it had a triple bond, it would have been called an alkyne and there would have been two less hydrogens. The other hydrocarbon that is not an alkane is a ring structure such as benzene.

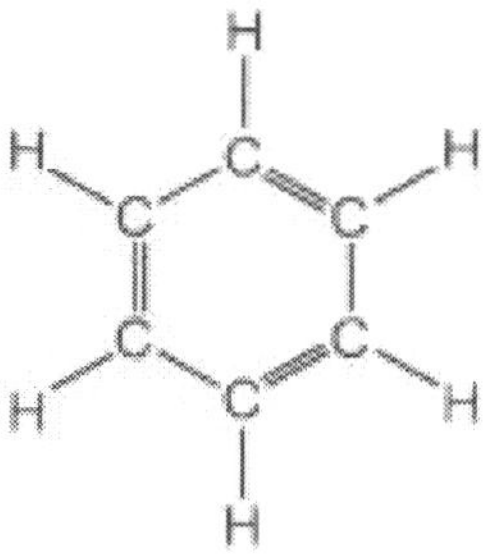

Benzene ring

Organic Functional Groups:

Organic compounds beyond hydrocarbons are called functional group compounds because within each functional group the compound reacts the same way. The functional groups are:

Halocarbons
Alcohols
Ethers
Aldehydes
Ketones
Carboxylic acids
Amines
Amides

Functional Groups	R stands for carbon chain or ring[1]	Example	Name of Compou
Halocarbons	RCl, RF, RBr, RI	CH_3Cl	Methyl chloride
Alcohols	ROH	CH_3CH_2OH	Ethyl alcohol
Ethers	ROR	CH_3OCH_3	Dimethyl ether
Aldehydes	RCHO	CH_3CHO	Ethanal
Ketones	RCOR	CH_3COCH_3	Propanone
Carboxylic acids	RCOOH	$CH3(CH2)_2COOH$	Butanoic acid
Ester	RCOOR	$CH_3COOCH_2CH_3$	Ethy ethanoate
Amines	RNH_2	$CH_3CH_2NH_2$	Ethylamine
Amides	$RCONH_2$	CH_3CONH_2	Ethanamide

In the case of methyl chloride the CH_3 is R and in the case of Ethyl alcohol it is CH_3CH_2 and so on for each compound.

This chart needs some explanation. Chemists use capital R for any chemical chain or ring. This is how your chemistry book will show these when demonstrating how these functional groups react. We will use the exact same format.

First, let's look at methyl chloride. In methyl chloride the methyl group (CH3) is R. In the case of ethyl alcohol ($CH3CH_2$) the ethyl group is R. You will need to memorize these functional group configurations in organic chemistry. Let's take them one by one and show reactions:

Halocarbons:

$$R\text{-}H + X_2 \xrightarrow[\text{light}]{\text{UV}} RX + HX$$

This is the chemist's demonstration of how halocarbons are made. R stands for any carbon chain or ring and X stands for any halogen like chlorine or bromine, etc. For the reaction to occur it has to be in the presence of ultraviolet light. Let's do the simplest possible example as follows using methane and chlorine:

$$CH_4 + Cl_2 \xrightarrow[\text{light}]{\text{UV}} CH_3Cl + HCl$$

Methane and chlorine in the presence of UV light forms methyl chloride plus hydrochloric acid.

Problem 11:

Show how you would make propyl chloride.

Solution:

First, put the question down in equation form just like you did in algebra and geometry as follows:

Make $CH_3CH_2CH_2Cl$

Now write the equation

$$CH_3CH_2CH_2CH_3 + Cl_2 \xrightarrow[\text{Light}]{\text{UV}} CH_3CH_2CH_2Cl + HCl$$

This is exactly how you might see this on a test. As long as you have memorized the naming you will know what they are asking. And as long as you know the few functional group reactions that are taught to you, you will be fine. It may look overwhelming at this point, but it's not. There are only a very few functional group reactions that you will have to know in high school chemistry. In fact, one reaction covers the basics for three functional groups.

RCOOH + RCOH --> RCOOR + H_2O

This one reaction covers the functional carboxylic acid (RCOOH), the alcohol (RCOH) and the ester (RCOOR).

Let's look at this reaction in more graphic terms as follows:

```
  O          H           O
  ||         |           ||
R-C-OH + R-C-OH --> R-C-OR + H2O
             |
             H
```

Carboxylic acid plus alcohol yields an aldehyde plus water

In fact for most tests this is the way you must show your work. Plus it is easier to understand in this format. Let's do a problem.

Problem 12:

What occurs when you mix propionic acid and ethyl alcohol. Show the reaction.

Solution:

First write the question out:

```
  H H O       H H
  | | ||      | |
H-C-C-C-OH + H-C-C-OH -->
  | |         | |
  H H         H H
```

Propionic Acid   Ethyl alcohol

Then solve the equation showing what it would yield

```
  H H O        H H          H H O   H H
  | | ||       | |          | | ||  | |
H-C-C-C-OH + H-C-C-OH -> H-C-C-C-O-C-C-H + H2O
  | |          | |          | |     | |
  H H          H H          H H     H H
```

Propionic acid Ethyl alcohol Ethyl Propionate

Mixing propionic acid and ethyl alcohol yields ethyl propionate.

The same equation to make Ethyl Propionate can be rewritten slightly different to better show the way the reaction went. By just rewriting the ethyl alcohol atom by turning it around so the hydroxyl group is on the left doesn't change the actual atom one bit, but it can then demonstrate how water is removed to form the ester as follows:

```
  H H O          H H               H H O   H H
  | | ||         | |               | | ||  | |
H-C-C-C-OH + OH-C-C-H -> H2O + H-C-C-C-O-C-C-H
  | |            | |               | |     | |
  H H            H H               H H     H H
```

This should make it easier to "see" what actually happened. The hydrogen on the alcohol grabbed the hydroxyl on the acid and turned it into water. Then the remaining unfulfilled oxygen from the alcohol bonded with the unfulfilled carbon of the acid. Remember we said that the carbon had to always have four bonds. The only way for the carbon on the acid to do this was to grab the second bond (now free) of the oxygen on the alcohol. Oxygen requires two bonds.

One last reaction and then you will be truly ready. This reaction is called polymerization. It takes two chemicals in the presence of a catalyst and or heat to form a multi-chain polymer. This is how plastics like polyester and nylon are formed. We will do nylon and show how this reaction occurs and then that will round out the compressed course in chemistry to prepare you for your A in chemistry.

The generic reaction to produce nylon using our friend R is shown in the illustration. In this case there are two R's, one designated R and the other R^1.

$$n\ HO-\overset{O}{\overset{\|}{C}}-R-\overset{O}{\overset{\|}{C}}-OH + n\ H_2N-R'-NH_2 \longrightarrow \left[-\overset{O}{\overset{\|}{C}}-R-\overset{O}{\overset{\|}{C}}-\underset{H}{N}-R'-\underset{H}{N}- \right]_n + 2\ H_2O$$

In nylon 6,6 the R is a four carbon alkane and R^1 is a 6 carbon alkane. In the bullet proof Kevlar fibers, the R and R' are benzene rings.

Nylon was invented in 1935 by the DuPont labs under the supervision of Wallace Carothers. In 1939 nylon stockings were introduced to women and they just went wild buying these up. However, when World War II broke out in 1941, there was a serious need for silk from the far eastern silk worm for parachutes. Since we couldn't get silk because the Japanese controlled this region, the women of America gave up their nylon stockings, which could be made into parachutes and tents. Thus the women of America saved the day with their nylon stockings. Just thought it would be nice to throw in a piece of history.

Summary:

You now have a basic understanding of Chemistry. You know what it is going to look like because you have now seen the Reader's Digest version that is the short version for the year-long course. Some of the examples shown to you were on a high level and some on a simple level. School will fill in the spaces between the simple and complex.

With practice this will become second nature. You will look at a periodic table and it will make sense. You will see an equation and the items will be familiar. This overview will give you a leg up on doing well in Chemistry. The biggest thing is practice, practice, practice the chemical equations and understand the concept of ions and memorize the names and rules of chemistry. The methods and techniques described in this book will net you an A if followed.

Also, don't think because you were not good in math in the past that you are going to be poor in Chemistry. This is definitely not the case. You could have been mediocre in math in the past and very well become an A student in Chemistry. It's a whole new ball game.

It's not about how smart you are, but how you utilize your time and how persistent you are in going after that A. Remember the teacher is supposed to be there for you. Don't be bashful to take full advantage of his or her time to help you. A good teacher will be happy to help. The good ones went into teaching for the satisfaction of seeing their students learn. In most cases you are doing a teacher a favor by being interested enough to seek help and to ask questions. Teachers are human. It saddens them when students are not interested. They feel that they have failed. And be sure to thank them when you get help.

Remember, this country needs more of you to go into math and science. It's where the jobs are going to be created. It's where the world can be made a better place and it's where the United States can stand tall amongst the other nations and remain competitive.

Best of luck and success to you,

John D. Forlini

Appendix A

Steps to Solve Word Problems:

1. First and foremost figure out what the problem wants from you. Sounds simple, but half the time this is where we fall down. Write down what units the answer should be in. If they want an equation write down what the equation should look like.
2. Ignore the unnecessary stuff in the word problem. Don't let stuff that is not essential confuse you.
3. If possible draw a picture that is representative of the question.
4. Set up an equation or equations that satisfy the request and given information. Sometimes just putting the problems words into an equation will give you the guidance to solve the problem as will a good drawing.
5. You will always hit that awful problem that you just can't see how to do. Don't waste time on this one, go to the next one. Remember on an ACT entrance exam or other exam most of the time every problem has equal weight. So put this one aside for later. The brain is an amazing entity. Sometimes while you are working on other problems, your brain will be unconsciously working out the solution to the problem.
6. Check your work quickly by substituting your answer back into the original equation if it makes sense.
7. Look at your answer and ask yourself if it makes sense.

CHAPTER 6 PHYSICS

FIRST: If you haven't already done so, go back and read the section on "The purpose of this book" and "The Introductory Overview" before you start. Most important, if you are a student, go back and read Chapter 2 " For Students". It's only 2 pages.

So what is Physics really about?

In a nutshell, it is the study of the physical world. This includes energy, matter, electricity, forces like gravitational forces, and mechanics of motion, light, and nuclear and atomic dynamics.

The high school course in physics is divided into five distinct areas. These are:

1. Mechanics including motion and gravity
2. States of Matter including thermal energy laws
3. Physics of sound and light
4. Electricity and Magnetism
5. Theories and explanation of non-classic theories

We will cover these five subjects individually to prepare the student for high school physics. This book is set up to cover each subject in the sequence shown because most physics teachers and physics books follow this.

The first 4 distinct areas above cover what is called classic physics. This is the physics that has been taught for the past 100 or more years. This classical physics is solid and proven and describes the phenomenon of the majority of activities. However, it did not satisfy the observations and activities of the very small or the very large phenomenon in the universe.

By very small we are talking about sub atomic and by very large we are talking about the universe and its origins. With the advent of computers and ever developing instruments to measure and explore physicists are making more and more discoveries and observations in this small and large region.

Physics has always been a science in which theories were made about physical observations and then the physicist proceeded to either prove or disprove the theories through experimentation. Out of this effort, laws of physical science were developed that are now considered the classic physics that students of the past are familiar with. Laws of force and motion for instance were made this way. Laws of gravitational forces are one example. Newton's laws of motion are another. The year in physics will devote the majority of its teaching through problems for the student to solve using these laws and formulas.

However, as stated subatomic and galaxial phenomenon don't neatly fit these classic physical laws. The last segment of this chapter on physics will cover these latest discoveries and theories so that the student will be aware of the latest developments in such things as quantum theory, the theory of relativity, and the "big bang". The combination of chemistry and physics describe the world we live in. There is some overlap especially in the atomic arena, but the two sciences are distinct and as mentioned describe the world that we can see and the world that we cannot.

Objective of this section of the book on Physics:

There is only one objective to this section of the book. That is to provide you with the insight and the methods and techniques to get an A in Physics. If you have read the two page chapter "For Students" you will know why. Even if you only obtained mediocre grades in earlier subjects, you can obtain an A in Physics if you read this overview of physics and – if you practice the problems, and use the method and technique to be described in this chapter before starting your Physics course. This section of the book will give you the template for the course.

What you do now will make all the difference when you sit down on your first day of Physics class in your high school. This book is designed to provide just the right amount of material to keep the student's attention without overwhelming him or her with too much material.

The ideal time to read this material and practice the problems and solutions is the summer before you take the course. It is also best to read and study this material in short intervals, perhaps a half hour at a time. Do the presented problems over and over. There are only 21, but they are comprehensive so that if you can do these you will be more than prepared. After you have seen the solution to a problem, come back to the problem the next day and try to do it without looking at the solution. The more you do this the more it will sink in and the greater your chance of an A in the course.

Things You Need to Know Before You Even Start.

First thing you need to know is that physics and the high school course in physics consists of a great deal of formulas and problems. Whereas chemistry was filled with chemical equations, physics is filled with formulas and problems. The best way to get an understanding of physics is to do all the problems and then do the ones you had trouble with over again until it sinks in. A year's worth of physics has been compressed into 21 problems to put you on a path to earn an A when you get to class.

Terms and definitions in Physics:

Providing definitions of terms in chemistry was a worthwhile procedure in learning chemistry. That is why I devoted the initial part of the chapter on chemistry to definitions of terms. However, reading a list of terms in physics would only confuse the student. Instead, I am going to tell you to truly be conscientious about doing the problems. You will learn more from doing problems and most tests in physics revolve around doing problems. Learn the formulas and do the problems. I can state this because this is what I did and I got an A in high school physics. We will include pertinent definitions in the problems themselves rather than separate them out.

I also had a fantastic physics teacher, Mr. Patrick. I have never been able to thank him, but he had a dramatic impact on my life. You see, I was not a "brainy" student. I enjoyed high school social life. I was in a high school fraternity, dated often, ran on the cross country team and played intra mural sports. I also worked during high school so I could buy myself an old car that I learned to keep going. None of these things was bad, but I could have been a great deal more focused on school work. I admit that I sloughed off more than I should have. But Mr. Patrick's presentation of physics caught my attention.

Method and technique to make an A in Physics:

If I had to do it over again, I would have been more conscientious in high school. I believe any person that you talk to over the age of 30 and especially over the age of 50 will say the same thing. They wish they would have been more conscientious. Being conscientious is not necessarily working harder or longer, but working smarter. The following information is the best method I know of in the arena of working smarter and getting the most out of your time and effort in math and science.

1. First, get a notebook that is bound. One that you will not lose the pages.
2. Take notes on one side of the page, leaving the other blank. You can take your notes on the right side or the left depending on which is easier for you. I always used the left side.
3. Purchase a good red marking pen.
4. As quickly after class as possible fix your illegible notes. I used to stay in the seat for 5 minutes before running to the next class. I would use my red pen to mark my notes so I could decipher them later on. When you are hurrying to take notes sometimes what seems clear when you are writing cannot be understood when you get home. But it is most likely still fresh in your mind right after class so now you can write over an illegible word or symbol in red to make it clear for later. If you wait too long you will wonder what the heck you wrote.
5. Before you start any other homework from other subjects copy your physics notes from one side of the page to the other. This reinforces what you have learned in class and makes it much neater. By having both pages side by side you can always refer to the original if you copied wrong. I always gave myself a treat when I started doing the copying. When I sat down to do physics I had a coke and a candy bar. It was my special time. Now a coke and a candy bar would give me heartburn, but I was younger then. I did the same thing when I took algebra and geometry.
6. After you have copied your notes, then do your physics homework problems. **DO THEM ALL.** Don't be lulled into false security because they seem redundant. Some may be redundant and some may have just a slight

trick to them that you would not have caught if you skipped the problem.

7. Check your answers. If you got it wrong, fix it and highlight it in yellow. If you can't figure it out and have struggled with it, then the next day in class the light will shine when your teacher goes over it. But do your best to struggle if necessary to figure it out.
8. Highlight the problems that you missed.
9. Redo the highlighted problems that you missed first time.
10. Write down in red on the problem itself any questions you might have so you can ask them in class.
11. Now you are ready for class.
12. The teacher will likely go over homework and then present new material. If you have done everything above, you will find that it is just refreshing to go over the homework problems that you have already done.
13. Don't get cocky.
14. When you study for your test do practice problems from your homework, especially the ones that were highlighted in yellow. If you miss one, mark it in some way and do it again before the test.
15. This next item can very well make the difference between a B and an A. Many teachers will give students their test back. So if you can find someone from the previous year who still has their tests, get their test and make sure you can do every problem on it. The teacher will not give the same test to you, but knowing how to do the previous year's test is a great way to help know what the teacher considers important. It is a great learning tool. Don't shirk on this one. Find someone who has taken these tests.
16. Smile when your paper comes back with a nice high mark. Because if you follow the above this is what is going to happen.
17. When you do well be prepared for your friends and peers to give you a hard time. Just tell them you find physics fun just like a video game. That should shut them up. Don't let them discourage you or make you feel bad for doing well. Just know that they are jealous and would never admit it. Ten years from now when you have the nice home, the great car and boat, and the great

significant other, what they think now will be totally insignificant and meaningless.

18. One last thing–Don't miss one class. You can catch up in history or English, but physics is tough. It's probably 10 times harder than history. If you have to be out sick, try to come in for the physics class and then go back home. Your parents can write you a note. If you are in sports, try to fix your schedule to take physics in the morning so that you are not pulled out at the end of the day for a game or game practice. Some schools like to have special programs where a student leaves class for something. Don't get talked into skipping out on physics.
19. If your teacher is available for help after hours take full advantage of this. For some reason students in high school seem to avoid this teacher help. Maybe you have to ride the bus or his or her times for help are not good, but if the teacher does make time available for help take full advantage of it. You are crazy not to, especially if you want an A.

    Some teachers take email. This is a great way to work with your teacher. Some teachers are great and some aren't. Remember their job is to help you. Don't be bashful about getting help. Also, the internet is a great source of help. If you have a question, type it in in google. Sometimes the internet explains things better than the teacher. However, the teacher should be primary because he or she makes up the test and knows what is important.
20. One last thing. Occasionally, you will get a teacher who works directly off the book and has you turn to the page in the book and reads off the page and explains the course from the page itself. This makes it hard to do the notebook routine.

    In this case, I recommend using a pencil and writing your notes of explanation in the book margins so that you can understand it later when you study from these pages. You may end up paying a fine for doing this, but it would be worth it and you would probably be doing the next student a favor by writing good notes in the margin.

You should still look over your notes in the margins as soon as possible like right after the class, just like the notebook. You can then write your notes in a notebook when you get home or just reread the ones on the margin of the book. Again, do the problems. Keep a notebook for these problems so that you will always have them organized. Mark the ones you have trouble with and do these over again until you are totally comfortable with them.

Note: When doing homework, some may find that it works better to do it in pieces. Do some now, then take a break, and then come back to it. This is especially true if you hit a wall and can't figure it out. And you will hit walls. Everyone does. It's like going from one level to the next in a video game. When you do hit a wall, take a deep breath and try again or go onto the next problem and then come back to this tough one later. You could also take a break and then come back fresh. Taking a walk around the block is a great break. Or shooting a couple of hoops. Even doing a couple of pushups is good because it puts oxygen in your brain. Whatever works for you is best. The physical activity is good because it negates the potential weight gain from the coke and candy bar.

So what's the point of all this physics stu*ff*?

Well, let's do a problem for example:

Problem 1:

You have been chartered with determining the breaker size needed for a new modern kitchen at a house going up in a subdivision. You are told that they will have a very large double oven with a resistance of 6 ohms and a special refrigerator freezer that has a resistance of 10 ohms. Some stoves use 220 volts, but these are going to be special and use 120 volts. The only other items on this circuit are the kitchen lights with a total resistance of 24 ohms. The plugs will be on a separate circuit. You are specifically asked "Would a 30 amp breaker be sufficient for this circuit?"

Solution:

First, in high school physics you will get the formula for voltage. Voltage is equal to amperage times resistance (V=IR where V=volts, I= amperage, R= resistance). You know that the house current is going to be 120 volts and that the stove, the refrigerator, and the lights will use only 120 volts. You know that all three will be connected in parallel and not in series. As always in physics problems write the question in a drawing or in terms of a formula showing what is being asked for:

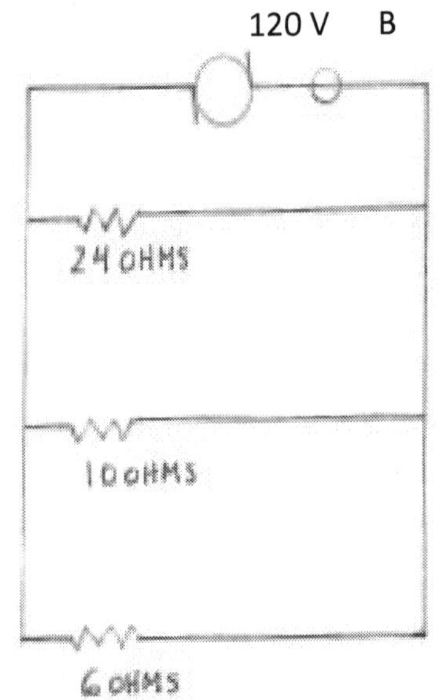

Determination of Breaker (B) Size

Amperage of B= ?

First, we know that the 120 volt supply from the power company will be attached to the 24 ohms of lights all in parallel, to the 10 ohms of the refrigerator in parallel and the 6 ohms of the special double oven stove in parallel. We thus made the drawing above to show the circuitry.

Each of the devices is a circuit in itself and will have its own amperage. Thus the 6 ohms stove is a circuit, the 10 ohms refrigerator is a circuit and the lights are also a circuit. Actually each individual light is a circuit, but since we knew the resistance of the entire lighting circuit we called this one circuit.

Finding the individual amperage for each circuit we employ the V=IR formula as follows:

Since V=IR, then

I = V/R

Stove:	120/6 =	20 amps
Refrigerator:	120/10 =	12 amps
Lighting:	120/24 =	05 amps
Total amps		37 amps

B = 37 amps

Thus, the total amps going through the circuit will be 37 amps. Depending on the electrical codes, the breaker could be 40, 45, or 50 amps. Below 37 amps the breaker will "trip" and shut the power off to this circuit. Thus your answer would be that a **30 amp breaker would be too small.**

This was just to demonstrate the kinds of things that physics can be used for in everyday life. And this is just a very small piece of the science of physics. Think of the physics involved in getting a space station in orbit. Or the physics involved in cell phones or the physics involved in building a sky scraper.

This first problem represents the kind of question you will see on tests in high school. In all likelihood the wattage and thus the amperage would be given on the base plate of the appliances, but for understanding the concepts, problems may be given like this one.

We will cover more in the section under electricity and magnetism. Don't be scared about this because you will have an entire year to absorb this in class. Having an appreciation of what the course is going to look like ahead of time will give you a major head start in your quest for an A in physics. Now would be a good time to emphasize that physical laws and formulas came from observation, then experimentation, then a hypothesis was drawn and tested until a formula was developed that could be used in all cases. This is called the Scientific Method. The actual definition of the **Scientific Method is – A systematic method of observing, experimenting, and analyzing to answer questions about the natural world.** You will probably see this on a quiz.

Before going on, it would be good to visit the reasons for doing well in physics and in science and math in general:

Other very serious reasons for doing well in Physics are:

1. Better paying career job out of high school.
2. For those going to college, it will provide opportunity for serious scholarship money. See the attached article from my local Birmingham paper about scholarships. The attached news article shows the amount for grade average and ACT scores (college entrance tests). For an ACT of 30 and a score of B+ in high school, the scholarship pays $ 9,000 per year. Even a B average qualifies. With a B and an ACT of 24 you get $3,500 per year according to the article. You have to be an Alabama resident or live in certain counties in Florida and Mississippi to qualify. Most every state has similar programs for residents of their state.
3. Doing well in Physics and math and science will open up doors in many fields like lab technicians, industrial chemists, pharmacists, medicine (from technicians to doctors), engineering, computer programming, technicians in all fields, technical maintenance of high tech equipment, technical sales, and much more.
4. Getting into two year technical schools. Technical schools enable their graduates to go right into high tech jobs that pay well and are extremely interesting. Industry is crying for these graduates and paying to get them. Many industries will provide tuition assistance to their employees to go to these schools. The key is to do well in science and math now.
5. Physics will improve the math skills that you missed or have forgotten from earlier courses. You will learn many of the things you had trouble with in the

past. Just keep a red pen to mark those things that you have forgotten as you come to them in physics. Call them rules and memorize them. One of the best ways to memorize is to practice these rules with the problems given to you for homework.

6. Physics teaches you about reasoning and logical thinking and improves your concept of the world. It allows you to improve your mental muscles just like an athlete must work his physical muscles to compete in the world.
7. Most important it provides you with the understanding of the world around you. You will look at things differently and you will have opened up a whole new world and potential for a wonderful life.

Just as an example, supposing you saw a job ad in the paper or on line for an electrician's assistant. Now supposing you obtained an A in physics and truly liked the electrical part. Well, you could interview for this job and explain how you did well in physics and truly enjoyed the electrical portion. You might just start a rewarding career as an electrician. After working as an assistant you could take a test to obtain an electrician's license. You could go to a two year college and study to be an electrician as well. There is always going to be a need for electricians to wire houses and work in factories. Electricians do well in life.

However, if you decide to go to college, this next article may be interesting to you because it shows that getting good grades could equate to getting good scholarship money.

High-Quality Academic Programs and Great Scholarships for Birmingham Area Students!

NEW!

The University of South Alabama is pleased to increase academic scholarships for resident and non-resident students through the new

MITCHELL-MOULTON SCHOLARSHIP INITIATIVE

Available for 2014 High School Graduates. Apply today!

These are the scholarships listed from the University of South Alabama for Alabama residents plus Mississippi students from George, Greene, Harrison, Jackson, Perry and Stone Counties and Florida students from Escambia and Santa Rosa counties.

ACT Composite Score	SAT Equivalent (SAT Critical Reading + Math)	Minimum High School GPA	Annual Amount	4 Year Total Amount
33 or higher	1440 or higher	3.5	$11,000	$44,000
32	1400-1430	3.5	$9,000	$36,000
30-31	1330-1390	3.5	$8,000	$32,000
28-29	1250-1320	3.5	$5,000	$20,000
24-27	1090-1240	3.0	$3,500	$14,000
23	1050-1080	3.0	$2,500	$10,000

ACT Composite Score	SAT Equivalent (SAT Critical Reading + Math)	Minimum High School GPA	Annual Amount	4 Year Total Amount
33 or higher	1440 or higher	3.5	$12,000	$48,000
32	1400-1430	3.5	$10,000	$40,000
30-31	1330-1390	3.5	$9,000	$36,000

28-29	1250-1320	3.5	$6,500	$26,000
27	1210-1240	3.5	$5,000	$20,000

***Back to Physics*:** As mentioned earlier there are 5 sections that physics classes are divided into during the year, the first is part of the classic physics that has been taught for 100 years.

Section 1. Mechanics Including Motion and Gravity:

Velocity, speed, and acceleration:

First of all speed and velocity are not the same. This will catch many students on tests.

Let's look at their definitions:

Velocity is defined as the rate an object changes position. Velocity is concerned with **displacement.** Displacement is how far from start did the object go. For instance, if you walk around a block and end up where you started, you have a zero displacement and a zero velocity. You just haven't in essence gone anywhere. You travelled a distance, but not a displacement. You had a **speed,** but not a velocity. This is simply by definition. You will have the same situation with work and force. No matter how much force you exert on something, if it doesn't move, then you have done no work. You may have expended a tremendous amount of energy, but done no work.

For speed and velocity to be the same thing, they have to be measured over a straight line over the same distance.

Average velocity and velocity can be the same if the velocity is constant over the period. Basically, velocity is the movement for a place in time and average velocity is the distance from one point to another over a specific time. The formula for Average velocity is:

$$\bar{V} = \frac{d_f - d_i}{t_f - t_i}$$

where d_f and d_i are the final position and the initial position and t_f and t_i are the corresponding final time and initial time.

This is why formulas in physics are so important for the student to understand and know how to use. So let's do a problem that may help.

Problem 2:

Jim and Sue are running a 5k race. Jim likes to start way back in the pack, but Sue prefers to be at the front. Jim starts out at 1,000 meters back behind Sue. This is a significant distance because this is a very large race and the course is not as wide as other courses, such that those in the back of the pack take a significant time to reach the starting line.

The runners wear a race GPS device that records the time that they cross the finish line from the start to the end so that the runners way back are not penalized for starting late. Although Jim runs significantly further, we do not count this as an issue because he is only timed from start line to finish line.

Calculate Jim and Sue's average velocity and speed from when they both started if they both cross the finish line at the same time.

Solution: This is a trick question in that they tell you that they are only counted as far as the race goes from start line to finish line. Since the question asks what are their average velocities and average speed from when they both started, then we need to ignore the GPS start line to finish line. The question is really only asking for when each starts and finishes regardless of the GPS tracking device. So Jim starts at minus 1,000 meters and Sue starts at 0 meters. Obviously Jim is going to have to run faster (speed) to catch Sue at the finish line.

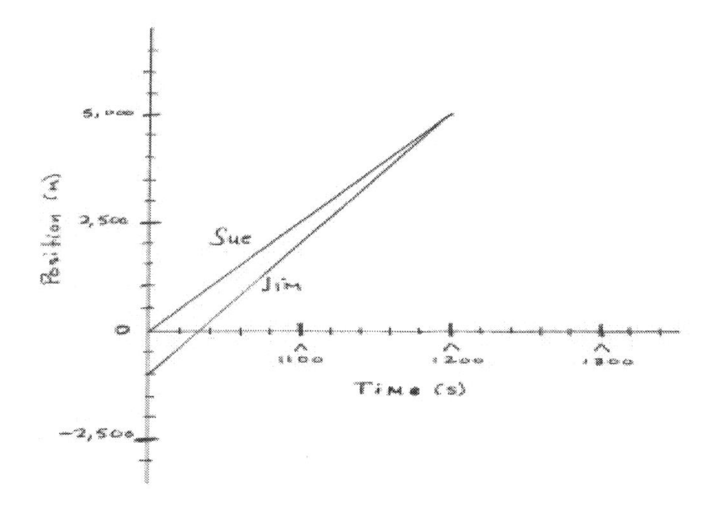

Let's do Sue first.

$\overline{V} = \dfrac{d_f - d_i}{t_f - t_i}$ where d_f and d_i are the final position and the initial position

$d_f - d_i$ is also called the displacement

So for Sue:

$$\overline{\mathbf{V}} = \frac{\mathbf{d_f - d_i}}{t_f - t_i} = (5{,}000 - 0)/\,(1200\text{-}0) = 4.17 \text{ m/s}$$

Now for Jim:

$$\overline{\mathbf{V}} = \frac{\mathbf{d_f - d_i}}{t_f - t_i} = (5{,}000 - -1{,}000)/\,(1200\text{-}0) = 5.0 \text{ m/s}$$

In this case since the distance is a straight line, then the speed and velocity are the same. Be sure to state this in the answer.

However, if Jim had traveled on a circular path for the 1,000 meters in which the radius of that circular path was 500 meters, then he would actually have travelled ½ x 3.14 x 1,000 m. The perimeter of a circle is represented by the formula $C = \pi d$, which in this case is 3.14 x 1,000. But since it is only half a circle then it is ½ x 3.14 x 1,000 m or 1,570 m. Thus his actual distance is now:

$$5{,}000 + 1{,}570$$

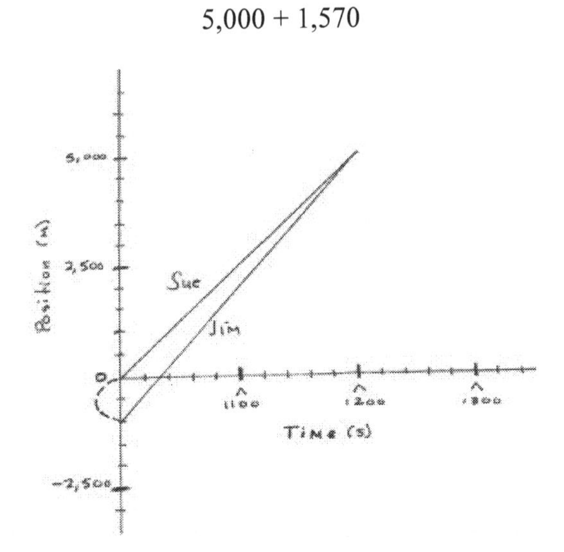

As far as the velocity goes, there is no change in Jim's run because the final and initial distance (displaced distance) is the same.
However, since he is going a longer actual distance his speed will change. He will in fact now be going 5,000 m plus 1,570 m. If he comes across at the same time as Sue he will have to be going much faster than he had before. Thus in this case the speed is total distance traveled divided by total time. Total time has not changed because he and Sue did the race in 1200 seconds.

So his actual speed is distance/time or 6,570 m/1200 = 5.475 m/s. Some definitions in physics are not readily intuitive. However, it is the physicist definition. We just need to go by his definition and his formula. The more we do this and not try to understand everything at once the more likely in the long run we will understand it and it will then become intuitive. Of course if it all makes sense to you right away more power to you. You will definitely get an A.

If the velocity of an object like a car or runner is constant, then there is no acceleration. A jogger running at 5 meters/s or a car at 100 kilometers per minute is at a constant velocity until there is acceleration or deceleration (braking or letting off the gas). In physics we call deceleration negative acceleration.

Acceleration is the rate that the velocity of an object changes or another way of saying it is the average acceleration of an object is the change in velocity during some measurable time frame divided by that time frame. Just like velocity, there is average acceleration and instantaneous acceleration. The formula for average acceleration (which is what most of physics covers) is:

$$\bar{a} = \frac{(v_f - v_i)}{(t_f - t_i)} = \frac{\text{rise}}{\text{run}} = m$$

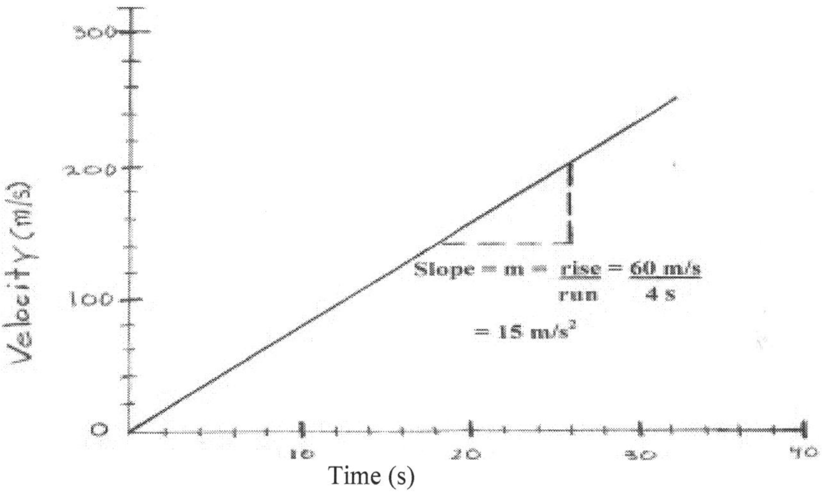

Velocity (m/s)

300
200
100
0

Slope = m = $\frac{\text{rise}}{\text{run}} = \frac{60 \text{ m/s}}{4 \text{ s}}$

$= 15 \text{ m/s}^2$

10 20 30 40

Time (s)

Some explanation is in order. First, remember back to algebra, geometry, and trigonometry and remember that a straight line was defined as a linear equation $y = mx + b$ where y is the y axis, m is the slope, x is the x axis and b is the y intercept. The intercept in this case is 0. So the slope m is $\Delta y/\Delta x$ or the change in y divided by the change in x or simply the rise divided by the run. Thus by definition the average acceleration is the slope of the line where y is the velocity and x is the time as in the graph shown.

Instantaneous acceleration is the tangent at a specific time. Since the average acceleration is a straight line the tangent would superimpose directly on this line and thus the tangent or instantaneous acceleration would always be the same for constant acceleration. For a curved line where acceleration was changing, then the instantaneous value would be the tangent at that point on the curve.

For now just remember that average acceleration is the change in velocity divided by the change in time for that period.

Problem 3:

A car accelerates from a stopped position at a red light at a rate of 6 m/s^2. How long will it take to reach 30 m/s velocity.

Solution:

As always let's see what we know from the question as follows:

$v_f = 30$ m/s

$v_i = 0$ m/s
$a = 6$ m/s^2

Since the formula for acceleration $(\bar{a})$ is $\bar{a} = \dfrac{(v_f - v_i)}{(t_f - t_i)}$

Then

$\bar{a} = 6$ m/s^2
$t_f = 30/6 = 5$ seconds

Check: Plug in the time:

$6 = (30\text{-}0)/(5\text{-}0)$ so it checks

The question could have been asked for negative acceleration in which it asked how long it would have taken to stop from going 30 m/s at a constant breaking at 6 m/s^2. Then $(v_f - v_i)$ would have been negative.

Acceleration due to Gravity:

Through observation, experimentation, and testing it is and has been for a long time known that the rate at which an object falls to earth is 9.8 m/s^2 and it is called the acceleration of gravity. Thus, as you know if you throw a ball in the air, the force of gravity will cause the ball to come back down. At the point where the ball starts to return to earth, the velocity increases by 9.8 meters per second. So the first second of its return it reaches a velocity of 9.8 meters, then at 2 seconds its velocity becomes 19.6 m/s and so on. So if you were to use the formula:

$$\bar{a} = \frac{(v_f - v_i)}{(t_f - t_i)}$$

And if you were to go to the top of a large cliff where there was no one below to get hurt and dropped a penny, then after 10 seconds it would have a velocity of $v_f = 10 \times 9.8$ m/s^2 or 98 m/s. V_i and t_i would be zero at the point you released the rock.

Force (F) and Force (f):

Force with the capital bold **F** symbol (**F**) is the force that has both size and direction making it a vector. A vector is any quantity that has both magnitude and direction. A velocity is a vector because it describes how fast and in what direction. A Force (**F**) is a vector because it also has a magnitude and a direction. Thus the F of gravity is also a vector and it is straight down. Now f for force is strictly the magnitude with no direction.

The idea of Force (**F**) as a vector means that forces acting from different directions on an object must all be taking into consideration to determine the actual or net force on an object. By looking at these as vectors, we can use simple geometry to determine net force on an object. The object of net force comes into play when for instance an airplane is landing. There is force of gravity straight down, a sideways force from the wind, and a reverse thrust force from the reverse engine thrusters.

Force is defined as mass times acceleration.

$$\mathbf{F} = ma$$

The greater the mass for the same acceleration the greater the force. A ten ton truck with the same acceleration as a Volkswagen Beetle will have far more force. By the same token two identical cars with the same mass will have different forces if one is accelerating at twice the rate as the other. This is intuitive.

In physics the force of one Newton is described as:

Newton (N) = 1kg of mass x 1 m/s^2
It is the force that moves a 1 kg mass at an acceleration of 1m/s^2.

Let's do a problem to see what we mean.

Problem 4: If Curly and Moe were moving a table and they were positioned on each side of the table and thus facing each other how much net force would be exerted if Curly exerted 100 N and Moe exerted 100 N? If Curly exerted 100 and Moe 200N and Larry comes along and helps Curly by adding 80 N of his own?

Solution:

First, draw the forces. Let's say 100 west for Curly and 100 east for Moe. The forces balance out and the net force is 0 N. The table doesn't move. Now in the case of Curly and Larry each with 100 and 80 combined force in the west direction and Moe with 200 east, the table will move west because Moe has 20 more N exerted than Curly and Larry.

Newton's Laws of Physics:

First Law: An object at rest will remain at rest until acted upon by an outside force. An object in motion will remain in motion until acted upon by an outside force. In other words, an object at rest will remain at rest as long as the net force is zero and an object moving in a straight line with constant speed will continue at the same direction and speed as long as the net force is zero.

Second Law: Newton's second law states that the acceleration of an object depends upon net force on the

object and the mass of the object. Furthermore, the net force on the object is equal to the mass times the acceleration or:

$$\mathbf{F}_{\mathbf{net}} = ma$$

For the force of gravity it is written $\mathbf{F}_{\mathbf{grav}} = mg$

Students have trouble with mass and weight, so let's talk about how much you weigh on earth. Obviously, up till now all you had to do was weigh on a scale and this was your weight. Well it still is as long as you and that scale are on the earth. Because your weight is a product of your mass and the pull of gravity by the earth. So if the pull of gravity were less like it is on the moon, then you would weigh less, but your mass would be the same.

Your mass is your guts and everything that is part of you that gravity acts upon whether it is measured in kg or pounds.

$$\mathbf{F}_{\mathbf{g}} = mg$$

$$m = \mathbf{F}_{\mathbf{g}}/g$$

In physics, you have to think in terms of Newtons and kilograms and remember the formula:

$$\text{Newton (N)} = 1\text{kg of mass} \times 1\ m/s^2$$

It is the force that moves a 1 kg mass at an acceleration of $1 m/s^2$. You could go on line and find conversions from Newtons to pounds, but for physics, it is best to think in terms of Newtons and kilograms because this is the definition used in this discipline and these are the terms that will be used on tests.

Problem 5:

Betty and Veronica are fighting over a pair of slacks with a mass of 0.2 kg at the store. They are both tugging at it trying to obtain it. Betty is pulling with a force of 12 N and Veronica with a force of 10 N. They are both pulling with a horizontal force. What is the horizontal acceleration of the slacks.

Solution:

As always write it out:

Veronica 10 N <__________Pants__________> Betty 12 N

Using Newton's second law where **F** = ma and rearranging

$$a = \mathbf{F}_{net} / m$$

$$a = \frac{\mathbf{F}\text{ (Betty) } + (-\ \mathbf{F}\text{ (Veronica)}}{m} \text{ East towards Betty}$$

$$\frac{12\ N - 10\ N}{0.2\ kg}$$

$$= 10\ m/s^2 \text{ East towards Betty}$$

Let's do a typical physics problem illustrating that you have to now think in these new terms that will seem foreign at first.

Problem 6:

Bill has a mass of 100 kg and is in an elevator on the first floor. He pushes the button for the 10th floor. The elevator rises at 2.0 m/s^2 for two seconds. During those two seconds what is the total of the upward force from the elevator and the downward force from gravity. What is the net force on Bill?

Solution:

First, put the question in terms of physics as follows:

$$\mathbf{F}_{accel.} + \mathbf{F}_g = ?$$

$$\mathbf{F}_{net} = ?$$

Let's do $\mathbf{F}_{accel.}$ First:

$$\mathbf{F}_{accel.} = 100\ kg \times 2.0\ m/s^2$$

$$= 200\ N$$

Then let's do $\mathbf{F}_g$

$$\mathbf{F}_g = 100 \text{ kg} \times 9.8 \text{ m/s}^2$$

$$= 980 \text{ N}$$

Thus

$$\mathbf{F}_{accel.} + \mathbf{F}_g = 1180 \text{ N}$$

But they also asked for the net force ($\mathbf{F}_n$)

Since the force of gravity is down and the force of the elevator is up

$$\mathbf{F}_n = \mathbf{F}_g + (-\mathbf{F}_{accel.})$$

$$= 780 \text{ N}$$

Newton's third law of physics: **For every action, there is an equal and opposite reaction.** Thus if you are pushing against a wall, you are exerting a force against the wall and the wall is exerting a force against you that is equal and opposite in direction. In other words all forces come in pairs. They are equal in strength and opposite in direction.

If you look at all of Newton's laws, it becomes apparent that forces are actually vectors and a resultant force can be obtained by utilizing geometry as shown in the next problem:

Problem 7:

An airplane is flying in a heavy wind that is blowing due north at 12 N. The thrust of the plane which is aimed west is 18 N. What is the resultant force and direction?

Solution:

As always, draw the problem:

The vectors are laid out tip to tail as shown below and then solved for the resultant force $\mathbf{F_r}$.

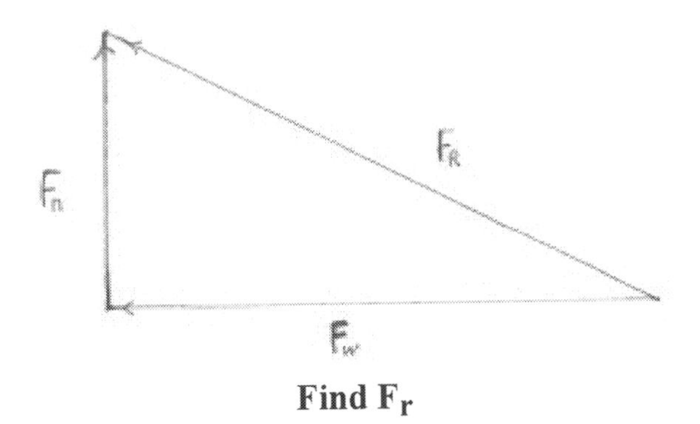

Find $\mathbf{F_r}$

Since this is a right triangle you can use the Pythagorean Theorem:

$$(\mathbf{F_n})^2 + (\mathbf{F_w})^2 = (\mathbf{F_r})^2$$

$\mathbf{F_r}$ = 21.6 N at the direction shown which is West by North.

Friction: Friction is defined as a force that resists the relative motion of one material sliding against another. There are two types of friction, kinetic and static. Kinetic is the friction that one surface exerts on another when one or both are moving as they rub against each other. Static friction is the force that one material exerts on the other trying to get it to move, but it is not yet moving. For instance, it would be the force you exert on trying to move a sofa that just won't budge.

Let's talk about kinetic friction. If you are moving an object at a constant velocity on a horizontal surface there are two forces acting, the normal force from mass and gravity and the kinetic force from the type of surfaces. Obviously, moving something over a sheet of ice on a pond is much easier than moving it on dry land. So there must be something that can be measured to give a relative measure of the differences between coarse and smooth surfaces. This something is called the coefficient of friction and is written as u_k for coefficient of kinetic friction and given by the formula:

$$F_{f,\ kinetic} = u_k F_n$$

There is also a coefficient (u_s) for static force. The static force only exists if there is a force on an object trying to move it. This static force is always less than or equal to the product of $u_s F_n$ since it isn't moving.

Problem 8:

If you push a 50 kg wooden crate across a floor that is also wooden at a uniform speed of 1 m/s in an easterly direction what is the force that you are exerting on the crate? The coefficients of wood on wood are:

0.3 for u_s (static) and 0.2 for u_k (kinetic)

Solution:

As always make a sketch and or show the equation to solve the problem.

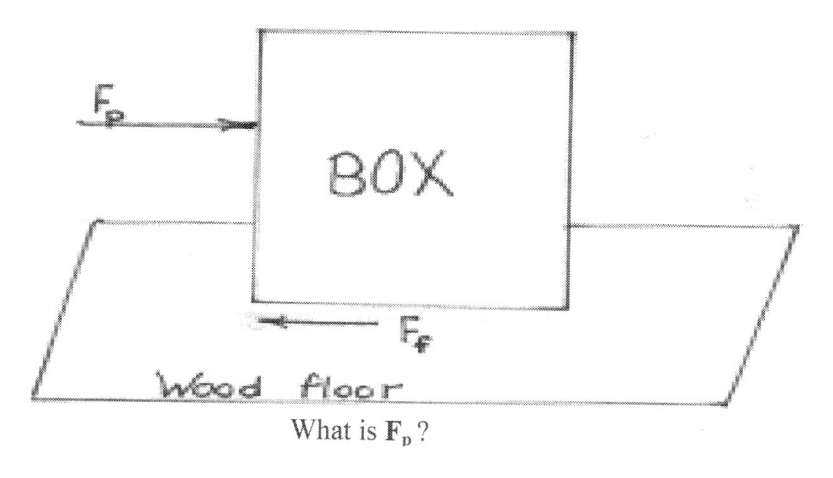

What is F_p?

Since the box is moving at a constant velocity the force we are concerned with is the force of friction which is equal to F_p. ($F_p = F_f$). There is no force of acceleration thus the only force is from gravity and

$$F_p = u_k F_n$$

Since F_n = mg (mass times gravity) the force bearing down.

Then

$$F_p = 0.2 \text{ x } 50 \text{ kg x } 9.8 \text{ m/s}^2$$

= 98 N to the easterly direction

Mechanical Advantage:

For centuries man has used devices to make his work easier. These devices may not be readily noticed in today's machinery, but they all come down to very rudimentary principles that have aided mankind for centuries such as the incline plane, the wedge, the wheel and axle, the pulley and hoist, and the lever.

The theoretical mechanical advantage of a system is the ratio of the force that performs the useful work to the actual force applied with the assumption there is no friction or that it is negligible.

Let's look at mechanical advantage for a lever for an example. To picture the advantage of a lever think of a children's seesaw. Remember the closer the person sat towards the middle the easier it was to lift him from the end of the other side of the seesaw by applying a downward force.

Force weight

^

w_1 d_1 F (fulcrum) d_2 w_2

^

In equilibrium (horizontal balance) the product of w_1 x d_1 must be equal to the product of w_2 x d_2.

Problem 9:

How long does a solid lever ($d_1 + d_2$) have to be for a man to be able to raise a1,000 kg object from the ground if a person is only strong enough to push down with a force of 200 kg? Assume the lever will need half a meter on each side for the placement of the object on one end and the hands of the man on the other end. Where would the fulcrum have to be placed? Show a simple drawing.

Solution:

First make a quick sketch.

Hands
1,000 kg
____
^

This is a pretty straight algebra problem. The formula to be used would be;

$$w_1 \times d_1 = w_2 \times d_2$$

$$w_1 = w_2 \times d_2 / d_1$$

$$w_1 / w_2 = d_2 / d_1$$

$$1{,}000/200 = d_2 / d_1$$

Thus the ratio of distance must be 5:1. Notice that this is the ratio of the effort to the resistance. This is also called the mechanical advantage. The definition of **mechanical advantage (MA)** is defined as the resistance force (1,000 kg) over the effort force (200 kg).

$$MA = F_r / F_e$$

The length would have to be six meters to get the ratio with an added 1 meter for the weight and the man's hands to each have half a meter. So the lever would have to be 7 meters with five meters from the man's hands to the fulcrum and one meter from the fulcrum to the 1,000 kg weight.

Check: 200 x 5 = 1,000 x 1

This is just one example of mechanical advantage.

Note: A smart man would get an even longer lever so he would not have to exert his full 200 kg of force. If he had obtained an additional 5 meters, then he would only need to use 100 kg. His MA would now be ten to one.

Energy, Work, and Power:

Work is defined as the displacement of a body by a force. There can be force with no work. If you push against a sofa and it does not move, then you did no work. So if you lift a book off the floor you have done work. The work is the force it takes to lift the book weight times the distance it is lifted. The formula is simply:

$$W = Fd \text{ (force times displacement)}$$

For example, if a force of 10 newtons (10 N) moves an object a displacement (d) 2 meters (2m) then it does work of 10 N x 2m = 20 newton-meters or by definition 20 joules (J). A joule is defined as one newton-meter. Since a Newton is a measurement of force as defined earlier.

Force in newtons = One Newton (N) = 1kg of mass x 1 m/s^2

Thus one joule of work is the equivalent of moving one kg one meter.

Work is also defined as a change in energy. For instance, the work-energy theorem says that

$$W = \Delta KE$$

Where KE = kinetic energy. So here work is defined as a change in kinetic energy.

Kinetic energy is defined as:

$\mathbf{KE = \frac{1}{2} mv^2}$ or one half times the mass times speed squared

So if you look at an initial versus a final energy, you get

$W = \frac{1}{2} mv^2_f - mv^2_i$ or $W = KE_f - KE_i$ or $W = \Delta KE$

Thus if a 2 kg object is moved 1/m/s then $K = \frac{1}{2}$ (2 kg) m/s^2 or

$$K = 1 \text{ joule of work}$$

These are all definitions.

Problem 10:

A young boy is peddling his 500 gram light weight scooter on a level driveway at a constant 10 N force over a distance of 5 meters. How much work does the young boy do on the scooter and what is the change in the energy of the scooter?

Solution:

The question asks for W and for ΔKE.

$$\text{Since } W = Fd$$

$$W = 10 \text{ N} \times 5 \text{ m} = 15 \text{ J}$$

Since $W = \Delta KE$, then the change in energy is 15 J

Power is equal to the work performed divided by the time it took to do the work.

$$P = W/t$$

Power is measured in watts. By definition one watt is one J of energy per unit second or

$$P_{watt} = 1J/1s \text{ or one Joule per second}$$
$$P = J/s$$

Problem 11:

A man lift in factory lifts Jim 10 meters at a force of 4,000 N in 20 s. What power does the lift motor use to take Jim up.

Solution:

The question wants to know the power (**P**).

$$\text{Since } P = W/t$$

$$= Fd/t$$

$$= \frac{4{,}000 \text{ N} \times 10}{20}$$

$$= 2{,}000 \text{ watts or } 2 \text{ kW}$$

These definitions of energy, work, and power will be used in physics in many problems. Be aware of these so that they will be familiar when your teacher reaches this portion of physics. Again do the problems because problems will cement and explain the relationships with greater clarity.

Section 2. States and Changes of Matter:

Heat Transfer:

Matter, made up of molecules can change its state (form) based on thermal energy. An ice cube can go to water and then to steam. These are the 3 different states of matter. The difference is the amount of heat energy that has been absorbed by each state. You add heat energy to ice and the particles begin to move faster because they have more energy. When they reach a certain energy level, they form water. As more heat is applied the temperature of the water increases until at 100 degrees Celsius or 212 degrees Fahrenheit the particles are so excited they break free and form a gas we call steam.

We mentioned Celsius (C) and Fahrenheit (F) because these are the two most common temperatures. If you took chemistry, you know how to convert from one to the other. Physicists have a different measure that is called degrees Kelvin (K).

Kelvin is graduated in the same units as Celsius but Kelvin starts at minus (-273^0) Celsius. So to convert from Celsius to Kelvin just add 273^0.

$$T_c + 273^0 = T_k$$

The lowest temperature that atoms of a substance can exist without movement is called absolute zero because their temperature cannot be reduced. Absolute zero is the point where the molecules are no longer moving. This turned out to be – 273^0 C and was designated as O^0 K the starting point for this scale. Thus to bring the temperature of Kelvin to the temperature at which water becomes ice you have to add 273^0. Thus ice and water together are 0^0 Celsius and 273^0 Kelvin.

The phenomenon of states of matter is that water as it starts to from ice has a temperature as it just starts to form from liquid that is the same until all the water has become ice. At that point as more heat energy is removed the temperature of the ice starts to drop. Conversely, when ice starts to melt it remains at the same temperature until all the ice melts and then the temperature of the water begins to increase until it hits the point at which it changes its state to steam.

There is a measurement that physicist call **specific heat,** which is the amount of energy that must be added to a substance to raise it one degree Kelvin. Every substance has a different specific heat. Water has a specific heat of 4180 Joules/kg of mass for each degree of temperature change and is written (J/kg)K. Aluminum has a specific heat of 897 (J/kg)K. The amount of heat (Q) transferred to a substance is given by the following formula:

$$Q = mC(T_f - T_i) \text{ or}$$

$$Q = mC\Delta T \text{ where}$$

$$C = \text{specific heat}$$

Note: Water and ice have different specific heats. Water as mentioned has a specific heat of 4180, but ice has a specific heat of 2060.

Problem 12:

Water with a mass of 1.5 kg is heated on a stove to make tea. How much energy is required to heat this water from room temperature (296^0 K) to one degree below boiling?

Solution:

What are they asking for? They are asking for Q to go from 296^0 K to 372^0 K (99^0 C + 273^0). Remember water boils at 100^0 C.

The formula to find Q is:

$$Q = mC\Delta T \text{ where}$$

C = specific heat (Don't confuse this with degrees C). From now on we will only be talking in degrees Kelvin (K).

$$Q = 1.5 \times 4180 \times 76 = 476{,}520 \text{ J or } 47.652\text{x}10^4 \text{ J}$$

In this problem we had a reason to only go the one degree below boiling. The next degree to get the temperature to boiling would require the same specific heat of 4180, but to go to the next temperature of one degree above boiling would require a significant increase in heat requirement. The reason for this is because the mass has changed state from water to steam. The particles in the water need additional energy to break free of its water to water particle attraction.

This energy to go from water to steam is called the **heat of vaporization.** It is the same phenomenon going from ice to water. The particles have to overcome their attraction for each other and this requires more heat than just raising the temperature a degree. The heat to go from ice to water is called the **heat of fusion**. This amount of heat is the same no matter which direction you are going. The only difference is that in one direction (ice to water) you are adding heat and in going from water to ice you are removing heat like a freezer in your refrigerator removes heat to make ice cubes. The magnitude of the energy is the same. This is also true of vaporization.

The heat of vaporization (H_v) for water is $2.26\text{x}10^6$ J/kg. It takes $2.26\text{x}10^6$ Joules of energy to change one kg of water to steam . The magnitude of the heat of fusion (ice to water or water to ice) is $3.34 \text{ x}10^5$.

Thus:

Heat to melt a solid is $Q = mH_f$ and

$Q = mH_v$ for vaporization

Problem 13:

You are in a restaurant and you have a pitcher of ice water on your table with 0.5 kg of ice in it. You pour out the water leaving the 0.5 kg of ice. How much heat will be required to convert the ice to water?

Solution:

Restating the question, "How much Q to melt 0.5 kg. of ice?"

Using the formula:

$Q = mH_f$ and knowing that $H_f = 3.34x10^5$

$Q = 0.5 \times 3.34x10^5 = 1.67x10^5$

Note: Anytime both water and ice are in the same vessel, the temperature is always 273^0 K. That won't change as long as there is any ice remaining.

Laws of Thermodynamics:

The first law of thermodynamics states that in a closed system, **the change in thermal energy of an object or system is equal to the amount of heat added minus the work done by the object or the system.** This is basically the law of conservation of energy applied to heat. The law of conservation of energy says that the total energy of an isolated system remains constant. It can be changed from one form of energy to another, but it cannot be created or destroyed.

Laws of Temperature, Volume and Pressure of Gases

Through experimentation it was learned that the pressure on a gas varies inversely to the volume of the gas. This is called **Boyle's law**. Thus if you squeeze a closed container of a gas the volume of the gas decreases. You have increased the pressure as the volume decreases as long as the temperature remains constant.

It can be written P = 1/V x a constant or PV = a constant

This is the opposite relationship between Volume and Temperature. As the temperature is increased the volume increases. This is **Charles's law.** Charles (Jacques Charles) experimented with the change in volume at different temperatures and recorded the volumes as he decreased temperatures. He found that the volume decreased by 1/273 of its size for every degree drop. While he could "cool" the gas just so far, he extrapolated down to what he believed would be the point at which there could be no more gas, which he then called absolute zero.

$$V/T = \text{constant}$$

Combining the two laws

$$PV/T = \text{constant}$$

And all gases have the same relationship so

$$P_1V_1/T_1 = P_2V_2/T_2 = \text{constant}$$

The constant is proportional to the number of moles (n) in the gas. (Remember from chemistry a mole is the amount of any substance that contains as many elementary entities (atoms, molecules, ions, electrons, neutrons as there are atoms in 12 grams of pure carbon 12.

The Ideal Gas Law is written as:

$$PV = nRT$$

So for an ideal gas the pressure (P) which is measured in Pascals (Newtons per square meter and labelled Pa) times the volume (m^3) = to the number of moles times a constant (R = 8.31 Pa(m^3)/kmol) times the temperature in Kelvin.

Problem 14:
A 40 liter sample of neon gas is at atmospheric pressure (101 kPa). The temperature is lowered from 200 K to 100 K and the

pressure is increased to 160 kPa. Find the new volume and the number of moles.
Note: kPa = 1,000Pa.

Solution:

V_2 = ? What we know is P_1 = 101 kPa, T_1 = 200 K, V_1 = 40 L
n = ? P_2 = 160 kPa, T_2 = 100 K

and we also know that R = 8.31 Pa(m)/mol x K and 1 liter = .001 m^3

We are basically increasing the pressure and lowering the temperature. Remember as the pressure increases the volume decreases. As the temperature decreases the volume decreases.

Since the relationship between pressure, volume and temperature follows the rule that the relationship of the gas has to remain constant in a closed system

$$P_1V_1/T_1 = P_2V_2/T_2$$

Then

$$V_2 = P_1V_1T_2/P_2T_1$$

= 101 x 40 x 100/ 160 x200 = **12.6 L**

So the new volume will be 12.6 liters

The ideal gas law is given by:

PV = nRT, thus

n = PV/RT

n = 101 x 1,000 x .04 m^3/ 8.31 x 200 = **2.4 mol**

Section 3 The Physics of Sound and Light

The Sound Phenomenon

Alexander Graham Bell invented the telephone in 1875. We have come a long way since then, but the principles of sound have not changed.

First let's show a diagram of the terms used in the transmission of sound waves. Whether they are through the air like a train whistle travelling down a track or a church bell or a telephone sound over wires or a cell phone sending sound signals off a satellite.

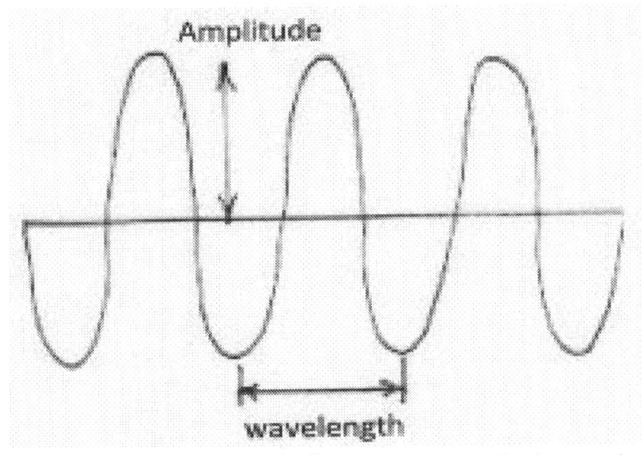

Typical sound wave; frequency = peaks/second

If you throw a rock in a pond, the ripples created continue until they just disappear. Sound waves have the same ripple effect. They ripple through the air. They ripple through water as in the case of sonar. They can ripple through metal as in telephones and microphones that convert the wave into an electrical signal that is then sent to a receiving device.

The three main measurements are the sound wave (wavelength), which as can be seen from the drawing is the distance from peak to peak. The amplitude of the wave is the distance of the peak or the trough from centerline and the frequency is the number of peaks per second.

Sound is actually transmitted by particles (atoms or molecules) in a solid, in a liquid, or in a gas by colliding into each other by the wave action set up by the source of the sound. The source can be anything from the vocal chords of a singer to the beat of a drum. It can be from a locomotive travelling down the tracks. If you have ever noticed that the sound coming at you as the train comes towards you or even an ambulance siren as it approaches gets louder and louder and then as it passes it gets lower and lower. This phenomenon is called the Doppler effect. The Doppler effect occurs because the sound waves are actually moved closer together by the movement of the train or ambulance and thus you have more waves (higher frequency) hit you per second and it sounds louder until it passes.

You probably have already learned from Biology that the sound waves that travel into the ear vibrate tiny little bones in the ear that then send a signal to the brain via a complicated series of nerves similar to how a diaphragm in Edison's phone vibrated against a magnet that then sent a signal.

Let's look at how the traditional telephone worked. The first thing that a sound wave (person's voice) came in contact with was a very thin metal flat round diaphragm about the size of a half dollar only paper thin. It was located on the inside of the transmitting end of the phone just past the mouthpiece. Behind the diaphragm was a small cup filled with tiny grains of carbon that pressed against the diaphragm. A tiny current that came from the telephone company went through the carbon setting up an electrical signal that was transmitted through wires to the phone company which was then sent to a receiver where a person was listening. As long as there was no sound waves hitting the diaphragm the voltage was constant.

The pressure on the carbon grains changed as sound waves made the diaphragm vibrate. A loud sound caused the sound waves to push hard on the diaphragm. In turn, the diaphragm pressed the grains tightly together. This action made it easier for the electric current to travel through, and a larger amount of electricity passed through the grains from the vibration of the diaphragm. When the sound was soft, the sound waves pushed lightly on the diaphragm. In turn, the diaphragm put a light pressure on the carbon grains. The grains were then pressed together loosely causing less electric current to pass through them, and less current flowed through to the phone company.

The phone company then sent this electric current (strong and weak) to the receiver on the listener's end. Two magnets were located at the edge of a diaphragm located in the receiving end of the phone. One magnet was a permanent magnet and held the diaphragm close to it.

The other magnet was an electromagnet. It consisted of a piece of iron with a coil of wire wound around it. When an electric current passed through the coil, the iron core became magnetized. The magnetized iron core pulled the diaphragm away from the permanent magnet. The pull of the electromagnet varied between strong and weak, depending on the variations in the current. Thus, the electromagnet controlled the vibrations of the diaphragm in the receiver and mimicked exactly the vibrations from the transmitting diaphragm.

As the receiving diaphragm moved in and out, it pulled and pushed the air in front of it. The pressure on the air duplicated the sound waves that were sent into the transmitter and thus the listener heard what was sent miles away. Now let's look at the physics of these sound waves. First the speed of sound in air depends on the temperature. The speed increases 0.6 m/s for every 1^0 C. At room temperature (20^0 C) speed travels through air at sea level at 343 m/s. The speed of sound travels faster in solids and liquids than in air because the atoms and molecules are closer together. Sound cannot travel in a vacuum because there are no particles to transmit the vibrations in a vacuum. Sound can be reflected back off walls or any solid surface. The velocity of sound is:

$$v = \lambda f,$$ where

v = speed of the sound
λ = the wavelength in meters
f = the frequency in Hz (Hertz = one cycle per second)

Problem 15:

A man standing on one peak of a mountain hears his echo from the peak of the mountain directly across from him. It takes two seconds for him to hear his echo. How far is he from the other peak?
Solution:

First what do they want:

Start ____________________>

Finish____________________<

The distance has to travel one second to the mountain and then one second back. Thus the distance would have to be based on one second. Since sound travels at 343 m/s through air, then the distance must be 343 meters.
Note: We have not taken the height of the mountain or the temperature into consideration, but you get the idea.

Problem 16:
What is the wavelength of sound in air of a 20 Hz frequency? Assume 20^0 C at sea level.

Solution:

We know that the formula for wavelength (manipulating the one for speed) is:

$$\lambda = v/f$$

$$\lambda = 343/18 = 19 \text{ meters}$$

The Light Phenomenon:

First, light travels in a straight line. While it travels in a straight line it does cast a shadow around an object that is called diffraction to represent some bending around the object.

For light some definitions are in order as follows:

Luminous Source defines anything that provides and originates light like the sun or a light bulb.

Illuminated Source is defined as an object that is illuminated by reflection from a luminous source.

Opaque objects are like brick and do not reflect light.

Transparent media are like glass and air that allow light to pass through them clearly.

Translucent media are like lamp shades in which the light can be seen, but it is not clear enough to see the actual source.

Luminous flux is the rate light energy is emitted from a luminous source. It is designated with the letter p and is in units called lumens (lm). A 100 watt household bulb emits approximately 1,750 lumens. This is the rate that light rays come out of the bulb source.

Illuminance is the number of light rays that strike a surface. Illuminance is designated with the letter E and measured in lux (lx). Lux (lx) is equivalent to lumens per square meter = lm/m^2. The surface area is considered to be the whole area that a source would hit. So if a light bulb were in the middle of a room hanging from the ceiling then the surface would be that of a sphere surrounding the light source = $4\pi r^2$. The equation for Illuminance (E) is:

$$E = P/4\pi r^2$$

Problem 17: What is the Illuminance of a surface that is 2 meters from the 100 watt light bulb.

Solution

The problem is asking for Illuminance E. Since the light is hanging into the room, you can think of it as illuminating on a round sphere that is "wrapped" around the bulb with a radius of 2 meters. It would be like the light was inside a ball in which the bulb is equidistant to the surface at all points. Using the formula:

$$E = P/4\pi r^2$$

$$E = 1750 \text{ lm} /(4 \times 3.14 \times 4) = 34.8 \text{ lx}$$

Plane, Convex, and Concave –the Basics:

Mirrors:

There are three types of mirrors as follows:

Plane mirror. This is your everyday flat mirror that you look at over your sink. Your image will always be real and the same size that you are and look like you, but if you held a written paper up to it, it would read backwards in the mirror.

Convex mirror. This is the mirror that is the shape of the underside of a spoon. It makes you look upright and smaller especially as you move the spoon away from your face. Your image is said to be virtual rather than real.

Concave mirror. This is the mirror that is the shape of the top of the spoon where you place sugar in. It makes you look upside down and bigger. Your image is said to be virtual rather than real.

Lenses:

Convex lens: Like a mirror a convex lens has a curve coming towards you in the middle such that the lens is fatter in the middle. A magnifying glass is a convex lens. Any boy or girl scout knows that you can start a fire by converging the sun's rays through a convex lens to a point on the object that you wish to ignite. The point at which the rays converge is called the focal point.

If you look through a convex lens the image of the object you are looking through the lens will appear upright and larger like a magnifying glass, which is a convex lens.

However, if you place the object more than twice the distance of the focal length, then the object appears smaller and upside down. A concave lens is like this () shape.

Concave lens: Like a mirror, the concave lens is sunken in so the middle is thinner than the edges of the lens. If you look through a concave lens the object that you are looking at will always look upright and smaller compared to the original. A concave lens is like this) (.

Discussion:

The best way to understand mirrors and lenses is to have a good laboratory demonstration. One of the things that does confuse students is that a convex lens will have the image that you see through it be upright at one point and upside down at another. This is not the case with concave. As we said, the image you see through a concave lens is always upright and smaller than the original.

The focal point of a lens and for that matter a mirror is the point in space where parallel rays meet after passing through a lens or bouncing off a mirror. To obtain the relative size of an image compared to the size of an object only requires a parallel ray and an angled ray. Remember the object is the actual item you are looking at through the lens and the image is what you actually see from your side of the lens.

The formula for determining the relationship between the object position and the image position and focal length is:

$$1/f = 1/di + d_0 \text{, where}$$

F = focal distance from the lens
d_i = distance from the lens to the image
d_0 = distance from the lens to the object

When the object distance from the lens (d_0) is exactly twice the distance that the image is from the lens (d_1) then the image and the object are the same size and the same orientation. When d_0 is more than two times d_1 then the image orientation is upside down. When it is upside down

The other formula is for the magnification (m) of an object:

$$m = h_i / h_0 = (-d_i) / d_0 \text{, where}$$

m = magnification
h_i = image height
h_0 = object height

Let's do a problem with a convex lens.

Problem 18:

A 6 cm tall object is positioned 36 cm from a convex lens that has a focal point of 9 cm. What is the image location? How tall is the image and is it inverted?

Solution:

First, sketch the drawing. Since the object distance to the lens is definitely more than twice the distance from the lens to the image, then the image is inverted.

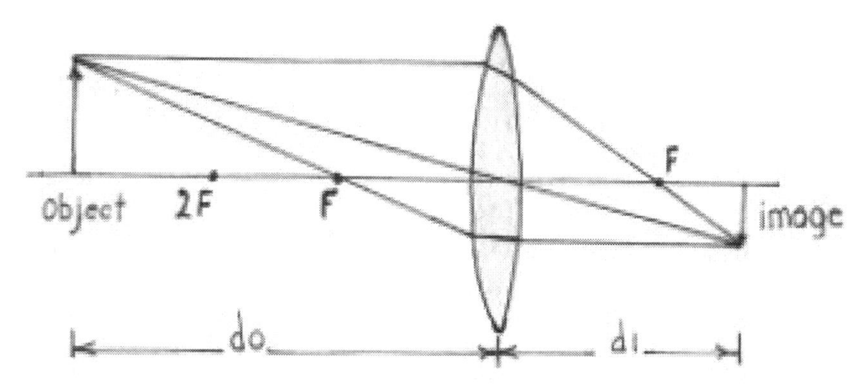

They are asking for d_1 and for the height of the image (h_i).

We know that :

$d_0 = 36$ cm
$h_0 = 6$ cm
$f = 9$ cm

Using the formula $1/f = 1/d_i + 1/d_0$

Multiply both sides by d_i and rearrange

$$d_i/f - d_i/d_0 = 1$$

factoring out d_i

$$d_i\,(1/f - 1/d_0) = 1$$

dividing both sides by $(1/f - 1/d_0)$

$$d_i = 1/\,(1/f - 1/d_0)$$

multiplying the right side by f/f

$$d_i = f / (1 - f/d_0)$$

multiplying the right side by d_0/d_0

$$d_i = d_0 f / (d_0 - f)$$

plugging in the known numbers for d_0 and f

$$d_i = (36 \times 9) / (36 - 9) = \underline{\mathbf{12\ cm}}$$

Now to find the image height use the magnification formula:

$$m = h_i / h_0 = (-d_i) / d_0 \text{ , where}$$

m = magnification
h_i = image height
h_0 = object height

$$h_i / h_0 = (-d_i) / d_0$$

solving for h_i

$$h_i = h_0(-d_i) / d_0$$

plugging in the numbers

$$h_i = 6(-12) / 36 = \underline{\mathbf{(-2)\ cm\ tall}}$$

the minus sign means what we already knew
the image is inverted.

In problem 18 we showed the algebra moves to solve for d_i. However, numbers could have just as easily been plugged into the original equation and then solved as follows:

$$1/f = 1/d_i + 1/d_0$$

$$1/9 = 1/d_i + 1/36$$

multiplying both sides by 9

$$1 = 9/d_i + 9/36$$

Rearranging

$$9/d_i = 1 - 9/36$$

do the math

$$9/d_i = .75$$

Multiply by d_i and rearrange

$$.75\ d_i = 9$$

divide both sides by .75

$d_i = 12$ cm and so it checks

Section 4 The Physics of Electricity

Simply stated, electricity is the flow of charged particles or electrons from one point to another. It can be static electricity like the shock that you receive in the dryness of winter after walking in your stocking feet across a rug and then touching something metal. As we learned in chemistry, it can be a current of electricity that is created in an electrolytic solution of ions in an oxidation reduction reaction. It can be a more sophisticated oxidation reduction reaction like the battery in a car and of course it can be the electrons going across a wire from a plug outlet in your home.

Static electricity:

Atoms can give up electrons or they can receive electrons. This movement of electrons from one source to another through air is called static electricity. When you walk on the carpet in dry air, your body either gives up electrons to the carpet or receives electrons depending on the material in your socks and the material on the floor.

The reason for this is that some materials give up electrons more readily than others. The point is that you would have gained or lost electrons. If you have wool socks and walk on a polyester carpet, you will gain electrons in dry weather. In normal weather with moisture in the air the moisture in the air prevents this exchange. Thus you either have a deficit of electrons or an excess. When you come in contact with another material like a doorknob this excess of electrons travels to the doorknob.

Electrons flow from one substance to another to try to balance the electrons so that neither has a charge anymore. For this reason two substances with different charges will attract each other and two with the same charge will repel each other. In physics lab you will have this demonstrated to you.

For now just accept that electrons that travel around the nucleus of an atom can be released and travel through a substance. Some substances release and accept electrons more readily than others and are called conductors of electricity like copper wires. Some do not allow this movement readily and are called insulators. Metals are good conductors because at least one electron on each atom of the metal can be easily removed.

When two objects have unlike charges this attraction to each other is a force. When two objects have like charges, there is an opposing force. This opposing force and attracting force can be measured and is given by an equation called Coulomb's law. This law states that a force (F) is directly proportional to the difference in charges (q) on two substances A and B represented as q_A and q_B the charges on each substance. This same force is inversely proportional to the distance (r) between them.

Coulomb's law is expressed:

$$F = K\,(q_A q_B)/r^2$$

When the charges (q) are measured in coulombs, the distance in meters, and the force in newtons, constant K is given as:

$$K = 9.0\text{X}10^9\ \text{N}\cdot\text{m}^2/\text{C}^2$$

Problem 19:

Two objects are 4 cm apart. Object A has a charge of 8 μC and object B has a charge of -4 μC. What is the force that one object exerts on the other and in what direction is the force?

Solution:

First, we must consider that the two forces are stationary at the point in time that the force is exerted. The second part of the question would be that the two objects force is towards each other since they have opposite charges. Remember 100 cm is 1 meter. Using Coulomb's law:

$$F = K\,(q_A q_B)/r^2$$

$$F = (9.0X10^9\ N{\cdot}m^2/C^{2)}\ (8x10^{-6}\ C)(4x10^{-6})/(4x10^{-2})^2$$

$$F = 18\ N$$

Electric Fields and Voltage:

When bodies are close together like the example in problem 19, the force is straight forward, but what about when they are far apart. When they are father apart how do you explain the change that occurs between two objects? What actually happens is that an electric field occurs around the object. This electric field is important because it sets up a level of energy within that field. This energy could be from a positive charge or a negative. An object in a uniform field would have work on it to lift it against gravity. This work if it is not used for moving the object creates a potential energy. The potential energy for a given charge is the ratio of the work needed to move the charge divided by the strength of that charge. Potential energy means a change in work per unit of charge.

In the physics of electricity this change in work per unit charge has been named the volt in honor of the man who did much of the work in this arena. The volt is defined as the amount of work in joules per the size of the charge in coulombs. By definition one joule per coulomb is one volt.

V = 1 joule (J)/1 coulomb (C) or

$$V=J/C$$

Thus voltage is an electric potential energy per unit of charge. If a unit of charge is placed in a location, the voltage indicates the potential energy of it at that point. It is a measurement of the energy contained within an electric field, or an electric circuit, at a given point.

Textbooks usually compare the potential energy of the volt to the potential energy of water at the top of a falls. At the point at the top of the falls, the water has a very high energy potential. In fact, when the water drops, this potential energy can be converted into volts by the water driving a turbine that creates energy by converting it through a mechanical motor that sets up a force field that then creates an electric current with a voltage determine by the resistance put into the circuit of this electric current.

For now let's go with the fact that voltage is the potential energy that can be used. It can be used to run a vacuum cleaner, light a bulb, or run an air conditioner. The volts have to get to these items and must have a flow density that is sufficient to do the work required of it such as the work to turn the vacuum motor.

One last thing on energy is the relation of energy to power. Remember from earlier the definition of power is energy per unit of time. It is the same in electricity. The watt and the kilowatt are units of power. A 100 watt bulb is the energy that the bulb is built such that the energy from a 120 volt electrical outlet will illuminate the bulb. This energy in joules per coulomb (volt) is the energy when multiplied by the amperage rate in coulombs gives power in energy per unit time called the watt. So a 100 watt bulb is designed with a resistance in its filament such that it takes .8333 amps and 120 volts to light the filament to the intensity to light the room. So that Power = volts x amps. Thus 120 volts times .8333 amps = 100 watts. Just remember P (watts) = V (volts) x A (amps).

There is a law named Ohm's law in which the relationship of this potential energy and flow density are defined. Remember all substances have conductivity. Some are extremely conductive like copper wire and some are more like an insulator and do not conduct very well. This resistance in a circuit is also caused by items that use the electricity. They represent a resistance as well. The resistance of a light bulb is caused by the light using the electrical energy brought to it to generate light and heat. Current flow is called an ampere. Thus the relationship of current in Amperes, Voltage (potential difference) and resistance (R) is stated as follows:

The current (I) through a conductor between two points is directly proportional to the potential difference (V) across these two points divided by the resistance (R) between these two points.

$$I = V/R$$

I is measured in amperes
V is measured in volts
R is measured in ohms

The formula can be rearranged to show that voltage is amperage (current) times the resistance or

$$V = IR \text{ (Ohm's law)}$$

In practical terms, the ampere is a measure of the amount of electric charge passing a point in an electric circuit per unit time and is defined as 6.241×10^{18} electrons per second, which is also one coulomb per second. The important thing is the use of this relationship ($V = IR$) in designing and working with circuits. For now just realize this relationship exists in the physical world. This relationship is called Ohm's law.

Now there is one thing that a student has to know as well and that is the difference between parallel and series circuits. A parallel circuit is one in which every item on the circuit receives the same voltage. It would be the same as all the appliances in your house being plugged into the wall sockets. All are connected in parallel because they are all receiving the same 120 volts. In point of fact this voltage, while constant in the house itself may actually vary from house to house by as much as 10-13 volts. So one house may be 110 v and another could be 120 v.

If you were asked to sketch a parallel circuit with two appliances (resistances) on it the drawing on the left is what you would sketch.

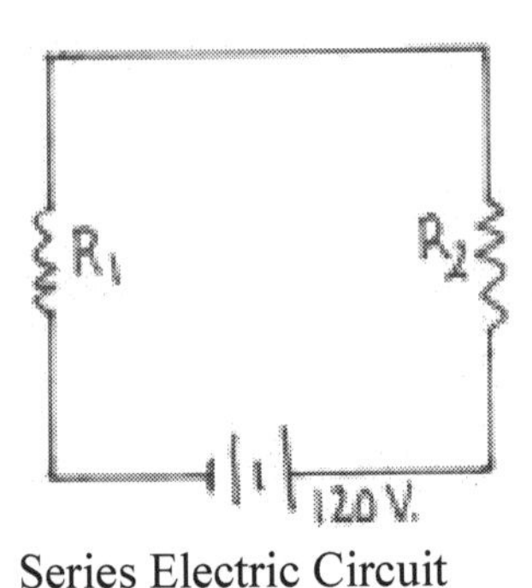

Series Electric Circuit

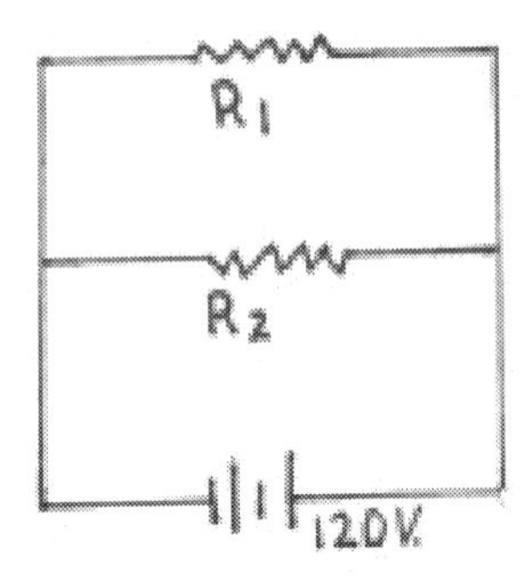

Parallel Electric Circuit

If you were asked to sketch a series circuit the drawing on the left is what you would sketch. Both circuits are receiving the same 120 volts. The two resistances on the left are receiving the same voltage, but the two resistances on the right are sharing the voltage.

Parallel Circuit:

The parallel circuit is the normal situation that you would find in your house. The two resistances shown (R_1 and R_2) could be two lamps or a lamp and a vacuum cleaner each plugged into an individual electric outlet. In an electrical circuit diagram like the one sketched, you have to just understand that parallel means both resistances are obtaining the same voltage. Even though it does not show two outlets, it does show that both are getting the same voltage.

Ohm's law states that the amperage going through the resistance is dependent on the resistance and the voltage. Both R_1 and R_2 have the same voltage no matter what their resistance is. If they were both the same resistance then they would have the same amperage. If the resistances were different, they would still have the same voltage, but the amperage would be different based on Ohm's law.

$$I \text{ (amps)} = V/R$$

Series Circuit:

In a series circuit the two resistances are not getting individual 120 voltage supplies. They have to share the voltage. The current flow is the same through each resistance and is based on the total resistance of the circuit (the sum of R_1 and R_2).

Let's do a problem to try to clarify.

Problem 20:

The teacher brings in two lamps from her home. They each have a 60 watt light bulb. Each is plugged into a light socket in the class and they are both turned on and lit up. To further explain parallel she brings in an extension cord that has three places to plug into. She plugs one lamp into one place and the other lamp into a second position on the same extension cord. Thus both lamps are getting the same voltage from the one extension cord. They both light up normally.

She decides to do an experiment. She removes the lamp plugs from the outlet. She then cut the plugs off both lamps. She then pulled the two wires that are part of the chord completely apart so she can get at each one. She then separates the two wires and has the two wires from each lamp coming out the back of the lamp so she can show the wiring separated more like a circuit. She then removed the insulation on both ends of the lamp where she cut off the plug. She then connected one wire from each lamp together by twisting the metal ends together and putting tape on them.

She then took one of the plugs she cut from the lamp, separated the two wires, and removed the insulation from the end of these small pieces of wire still attached to the plug. She then connected one end of the plug to the remaining wire of one lamp and the other end of the plug to the other end of the other lamp and carefully put tape around these individual spliced connections as well to protect her and others from getting serious shocks.

What will happen when she plugs this new circuit with the two lamps that are now in series back into the 120 v wall socket and what would you first notice about the intensity of the two lights. What has happened? What does the circuit look like? How does this compare to the original circuit that these two lamps were in before? What is the resistance of the total new circuit.

Solution:

It is always best to draw a diagram before you do anything else. So do a diagram of the two lamps.

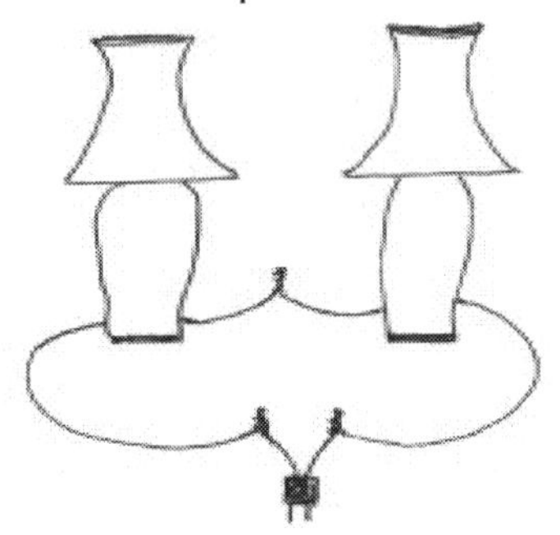

Rewrite the specific questions:

1. What happens when she plugs the new plug connection into the outlet?
2. Intensity of lamps?
3. Draw the new circuit.
4. Compare to original circuit.
5. What is new resistance of the circuit?

For the first question, we can easily see that what we have with the two lamps is a series circuit. We could draw this circuit as follows:

R_1 and R_2 are the two lamps

We already know that if she plugs this in both lamps will light. So the answer to the first question is that **both lamps will light**

We know that the two lamps will have to share the voltage because

V (source) = V for R_1 plus V for R_2

We also know that for a 60 watt bulb to burn with the intensity of illumination it was designed, it has to have 60 watts of power

Since Power is given by the formula:

$$P = I \cdot V$$

Then the power will be less than 60 watts because the voltage to each lamp is now less and thus lower illumination

Now they want us to compare it to the original circuit. The best way would be to sketch both circuits and label them.

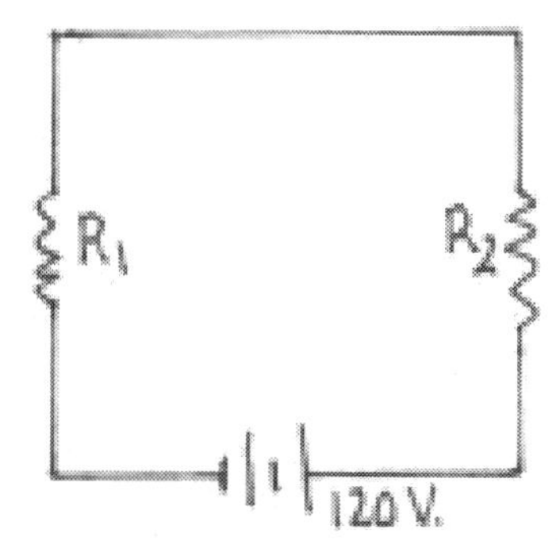

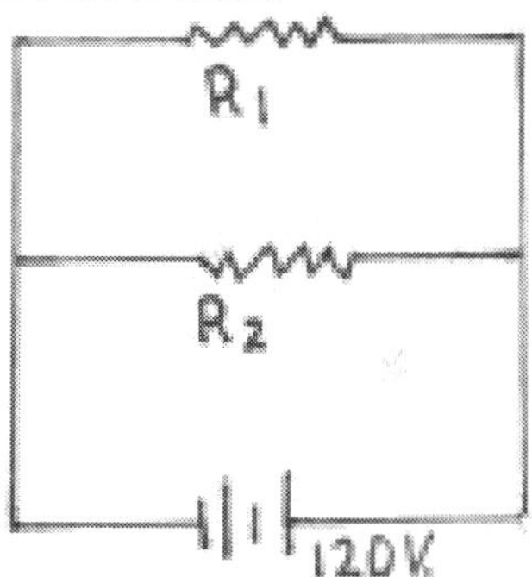

New circuit (series) Original circuit (parallel)
Where R_1 and R_2 each represent a lamp

The next question involves finding the resistance of the new circuit.

This is a tough one because we don't know the amperage of the new circuit.

However, we could establish the amperage through one light bulb because we know it would have to have 60 watts to burn with its designed intensity.

Since power is defined as

$$P= \text{Amps} \times \text{Volts}$$

Then in a simple house circuit,

$$60 \text{ watts} = 120 \times A$$

$$\text{So } A = 0.5 \text{ amps}$$

Using Ohm's law

$$R = V/A$$

$$R = 120/0.5 = 240 \text{ ohms}$$

We now have the resistance of one lamp, so the resistance of two identical lamps in series has to be the sum of their resistance, thus the total resistance of the series circuit is 480 ohms.

Problem 21:

How many 100 watt bulbs can you plug into a 120 v outlet before the 10 amp breaker trips?

Solution:

Find the amperage for each bulb and then add them up until they exceed 10 amps.

$$\text{Since } P = VA, \text{ then}$$

$$A = P/V$$

$$A = 100/120 = 0.83 \text{ amps}$$

Thus 10amps/.83 amps per bulb = **12 lamps (over12 lamps would trip the breaker)**

Another way to look at it would be 12 lamps x .83 amps = 9.96 amps, thus the next lamp would put it over 10 amps and thus trip the breaker.

Magnets, Electromagnetic Force, Generators and Motors:

In nature there exist metal materials that are magnetic. These magnetic materials have the ability to attract other metals. We have all had a magnet in our hands at one time or another. The thing about a metal magnet is that it is polarized. That is, it has opposite ends that are opposing in that electrons line up with an excess of electrons on one side and a deficiency on the other.

Physicists have labelled the side with the deficiency as the plus side or north side and the side with all the electrons is the south side. In a bar magnet you can easily see the force field that is set up by placing iron filings at each end. They will form a magnetic field. When a metal wire is passed through a magnetic field a current is set up in the wire.

This is exactly how a generator is made.

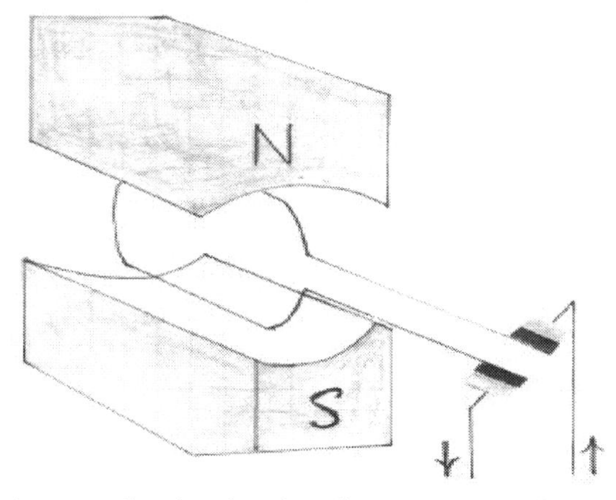

As the metal wire in the diagram turns from an outside mechanical force like a turbine driven by steam or water it spins the wire in the magnetic fields. The wire then cuts the magnetic field of the stationary magnets and a current of electricity is formed in the wire. An electric motor is the same thing in reverse. Instead of a mechanical device turning the wire, there is nothing mechanical to turn the wire, but a current is induced in the wire which then spins the wire inside the magnetic field. Another way that a generator or motor can be made is to have metal coils stationary in the place of the two magnets and have a magnetic bar spin inside of the coils of wire. The same principle of a wire cutting a magnetic field and inducing a current applies. In physics class you will study more about magnetic and electromagnetic forces and how to measure these. For now it's well to just know the concept.

An electromagnetic force can be demonstrated in two ways. The first way is to wrap some insulated wire around a nail and put a current through the wire. The electromagnetic force will turn the nail into a magnet because the electromagnetic force will polarize the nail with negative atoms on one side and positive on the other. The second method would be to leave the coil of wire by itself with no nail, but still leave the electric current going through. Then make up another coil and place it near the first coil with the electric current. You can measure the current and voltage of this second coil thus showing that the electric field in the wire was able to bridge across the air to the other coil. Depending on the ratio of coils of the original coil with an attached voltage and the coil placed next to it you will get a voltage based on this ratio.

In the drawing the loop of wire is spinning within the magnetic field developing an alternating current just like the current in a home. It is alternating because the wire is moving across the field first in one direction and then in the other, thus flow of electrons keeps changing. Since this flow is first in one direction and then another it is called alternating current.

Section 5 Non-classic theories

These first 4 sections make up 95% or more of the physics class curriculum subjects in most high schools. These first four sections describe the phenomenon of the majority of activities. However, we mentioned in the beginning that these standard well documented laws and formulas don't tell the whole story. They do not satisfy the very small or the very large.

By very small we are talking about sub atomic and by very large we are talking about the universe and its origins. With the advent of computers and ever developing instruments to measure and explore, physicists are making more and more discoveries and observations in this small and large region. Many new theories have been developed over the past years to try and explain these two areas.

The Very Small and the very large:

When we say very small we are talking about atoms and subatomic particles and how they explain observed behavior of matter and its interaction with energy and light. Some of you have heard of Quantum mechanics. Quantum mechanics is a body of scientific principles that attempt to explain the interactions on this sub atomic level.

The two major breakthroughs in this arena of physics have been Einstein's theory of relativity, $E = Mc^2$ and Quantum physics. Einstein's theory was developed in the first part of the 1900's and is given by the equation $E = MC^2$ where E is equal to energy, M is the mass and C is the speed of light. Einstein's theories have been used to describe the bending of light by very massive stars, which leads to a discussion of black holes. Basically the way I have seen it explained is that when a massive star uses up all its fuel and turns dark it also collapses on itself forming such a dense mass that it in effects sucks in all the matter from nearby particles in the universe and forms a huge body. Scientists are saying that this may be the reason that our universe is actually getting larger.

All of this is theory, but many of the theories explain phenomenon of massive stellar activities in the universe. Einstein's theory proclaimed that gravity is not a force, but the effect of space itself. Einstein theorized that mass changes the space around it. Mass causes space to be curved and other heavenly bodies accelerate because of the way they follow this curved space.

It would be like a person lying on a hammock and this indentation caused things near it to roll into the person because of the distortion to the hammock by the person.

The physics course in high school is not able to give a student any more than a rudimentary explanation of these phenomenon because it is so complex and requires a doctoral physicist to understand the principles and their interaction. However, some high school physics books will cover the theories to a small degree. Interestingly, over the years Einstein's theory has explained the massive phenomenon observed in stellar activities in the universe.

As mentioned quantum mechanics was the other major discovery since the classic notions of physics. It describes the relationship of subatomic particles and how they interact.

Quantum Mechanics:

Different types of energy such as light behave in some respects like particles and in other respects like waves. For centuries scientists debated whether light was a stream of tiny particles (photons) or a wave at different frequencies. Einstein helped to move scientific thought towards the photon model to explain the phenomenon of light and other objects exhibiting properties of waves sometimes and particles at other times.

Classical physics could not explain the relationship between temperatures and predominant frequencies of radiation. In wavelengths of short magnitude, energy should be emitted by a hot body at an infinite rate. It should have held true, but in experimentation after experimentation it did not. To explain this phenomenon a scientist named Max Planck developed a theory to explain the results. His theory which came from his experimentation with oscillators to produce different frequencies showed that each oscillator produced a certain quantity of energy based on its frequency. Each quantum of energy (beginning of quantum mechanics) was proportional to the frequency of the oscillator used. He developed the "Planck constant" that related energy to a constant times the frequency. This theory and formula netted Planck a Nobel prize in physics.

$E = hf$ where energy and frequency are related through a constant (h)

Einstein took this further and as mentioned moved scientific thought towards a photon model. He postulated that a beam of light is a stream of particles and agreed with Planck that each particle would have an energy equal to its frequency and that that energy would be hf. In prior theory the intensity of the beam should matter with regards to the energy imparted to the object. In fact and in experimentation this did not hold true.

What Einstein postulated was that a certain amount of energy hf of a single photon could only transfer hf to an electron. He argued that it takes a certain amount of energy, which he called the work function to remove an electron from a metal He concluded therefore that the intensity of the beam has no effect. In essence the amount of energy was determined to be in a quantum at discrete steps depending upon the frequency of the photon and this would determine how much energy it would impart to the electron.

The quantum mechanics led to the obvious conclusion that light particles exhibit both particle and wave motion phenomenon and that frequency plays a major part in the quantum transfer of energy. This may all seem like inconsequential theorizations, but these theories and work by physicist in the early 1900's and into the 20th and 21st century led to the laser, the transistor, the electron microscope, and magnetic resonance imaging.

Laboratory Work:

Laboratory exercises vary from school to school. Just make sure that you get the point of the lab and don't get too involved in the mechanics such that the purpose eludes you. Things don't always work properly in lab. Show the teacher that you are doing your best and **ask him or her for help right away if it is not going correctly.** And above all follow the safety rules that the teacher gives you.

The key is to know what the purpose of the experiment was. If you don't get it, ask the teacher what the experiment was supposed to teach you. Don't be embarrassed to ask.

Summary:

You now have a basic understanding of Physics. You know what it is going to look like because you have now seen the Reader's Digest version that is the short version for the year-long course. Some of the examples shown to you were on a high level and some on a simple level. School will fill in the spaces between the simple and complex.

With practice this will become second nature. You will learn many formulas and how to apply them. Application through doing problems will enlighten you to the meanings and value of these formulas. This overview will give you a leg up on doing well in Physics. The biggest thing is practice, practice, practice the problems. The methods and techniques described in this book will net you an A if followed.

Also, don't think because you were not good in math in the past that you are going to be poor in Physics. This is definitely not the case. You could have been mediocre in math in the past. This is no excuse not to become an A student in Physics. Use this new technique discussed to make an A in Physics. It's not about how smart you are, but how you utilize your time and how persistent you are in going after that A. Remember the teacher is supposed to be there for you. Don't be bashful to take full advantage of his or her time to help you. A good teacher will be happy to help. The good ones went into teaching for the satisfaction of seeing their students learn. In most cases you are doing a teacher a favor by being interested enough to seek help and to ask questions. Teachers are human. It saddens them when students are not interested. They feel that they have failed. And be sure to thank them when you get help.

Remember, this country needs more of you to go into math and science. It's where the jobs are going to be created. It's where the world can be made a better place and it's where the United States can stand tall amongst the other nations and remain competitive.

Best of luck and success to you,

John D. Forlini

Appendix A

Steps to Solve Word Problems:

1. First and foremost figure out what the problem wants from you. Sounds simple, but half the time this is where we fall down. Write down what units the answer should be in. If they want an equation write down what the equation should look like.
2. Ignore the unnecessary stuff in the word problem. Don't let stuff that is not essential confuse you.
3. If possible draw a picture that is representative of the question.
4. Set up an equation or equations that satisfy the request and given information. Sometimes just putting the problems words into an equation will give you the guidance to solve the problem as will a good drawing.
5. You will always hit that awful problem that you just can't see how to do. Don't waste time on this one, go to the next one. Remember on an ACT entrance exam or other exam most of the time every problem has equal weight. So put this one aside for later. The brain is an amazing thing. Sometimes while you are working on other problems, your brain will be unconsciously working out the solution to the problem you had trouble with.
6. Check your work quickly by substituting your answer back into the original equation if it makes sense to do so.
7. Look at your answer and ask if it makes sense and is in the units of the request.

CHAPTER 7 TRIGONOMETRY

FIRST: If you haven't already done so, go back and read the section on "The purpose of this book" and "The Introductory Overview" before you start. Most important, if you are a student, go back and read Chapter 2 " For Students". It's only 2 pages.

So** what **is trigonometry really?

The dictionary defines trigonometry as the branch of mathematics concerned with the properties of trigonometric functions and their application to the determination of the angles and sides of triangles. However, high school trigonometry takes it a step forward by covering logarithms and exponents, radians and circles and quadratic equations with some graphing thrown in.

Trigonometry is used in surveying and navigation and in other scientific endeavors that bring us new products and developments. Like all math it is problems, problems, and more problems.

Objective of this section of the book on trigonometry.

There is only one objective to this section of the book. That is to provide you with the insight and the methods and techniques to get an A in trigonometry. If you have read the two page chapter "For Students" you will know why. Even if you only obtained a C in algebra or geometry, you can obtain an A in trigonometry if you read this overview of trigonometry and – if you practice the problems, and use the method and technique to be described in this chapter before starting your trig course.

What you do now will make all the difference when you sit down on your first day of trig class in your high school. This book is designed to provide just the right amount of material to keep the student's attention without overwhelming him or her with too much material.

The ideal time to read this material and practice the problems and solutions is the summer before you take the course. It is also best to read and study this material in short intervals, perhaps a half hour at a time. Do the presented problems over and over.

There are only 14, but they are comprehensive so that if you can do these you will be more than prepared for your first day of trig. After you have seen the solution to a problem, come back to the problem the next day and try to do it without looking at the solution. The more you do this the more it will sink in and the greater your chance of an A in the course.

Things You Need to Know Before You Even Start.

Since this course is an extension of geometry, it would be wise to do a quick review and do two problems to help refresh your memory.

Quick Review of Geometry:

If it has been a while since you took geometry it would be wise to revisit some information from geometry and do a couple of problems before starting on Trigonometry. Trigonometry is basically an extension of geometry and may be taught as a separate course in high school or part of an advanced course in some other math program.

Triangles:

Triangles make up a large portion of trigonometry so we will start with triangles first. Let's look more closely at the four shapes of triangles and then discuss these.

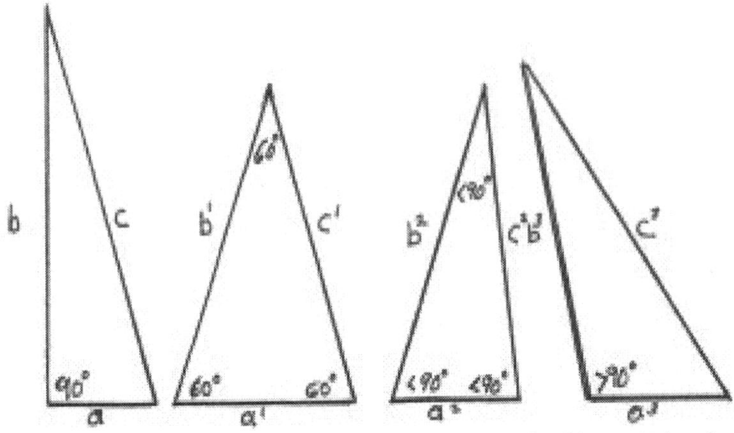

Right Triangle Equilateral Triangle Acute Triangle Obtuse Triangle
(Isosceles Triangle)

Right triangle: The definition of a right triangle is that it must have one angle equal to 90 degrees written as 90^0.

Equilateral triangle: The definition of an equilateral triangle is that all angles must be 60^0. Because all angles are the same 60^0 all three sides are the same length. So side a^1 is the same as b^1 and c^1 . The equilateral triangle does not look from the drawing as though the sides are equal. This may happen to you on a test where they show the drawing and purposely don't have it look equal. However, you just know all sides are equal because all the angles are 60^0. You have to know this in geometry and trigonometry. It's just a fact of physical laws, which we will explain further.

Isosceles triangle: You will note that under the Equilateral Triangle is the term Isosceles Triangle. By definition an Isosceles Triangle is one in which two sides are equal. In geometry the word congruent is used for equal. So that the definition is going to say that two sides are congruent. It could also have said that two angles of the triangle are equal because if the sides are equal so are the angles opposite the sides. So an equilateral triangle is also an isosceles triangle. But an isosceles triangle is not necessarily an equilateral triangle because the third side of an isosceles triangle could be different.

Isosceles right triangle: An isosceles right triangle would mean that two of the angles are 45^0 and the third of course is 90^0. This is because the sum of the angles of any triangle is always 180^0

and also because a right triangle must have one angle equal to 90^0.

Acute triangle: The definition of an acute triangle is that all angles are less than 90^0 as shown symbolically by $< 90^0$.

Obtuse triangle: The definition of an obtuse triangle is that one angle must be greater than 90^0 ($> 90^0$ as shown in the pictorial).

30-60-90 triangle: Triangle ABC has a 30^0, 60^0, and a 90^0 angle and is called a 30-60-90 triangle. What makes this right triangle significant is the sides are always proportion no matter what the size the triangle is. The ratio is always 1, 2, $\sqrt{3}$.

The 1 would be across from the 30 degree angle, the 2 would be across from the 90 degree angle and the $\sqrt{3}$ would be across from the 60 degree angle.

Scalene triangle: A scalene triangle is one in which all 3 sides are different lengths. Since if they are different lengths so are all 3 angles different sizes. Obviously an equilateral triangle cannot be scalene. The others may or may not be.

Polygon: All of the above shapes are polygons. A polygon is any two dimensional shape that has straight sides. Thus a circle is not a polygon because it does not have straight sides. Triangles, rectangles, etc. are two dimensional shapes that have straight sides. A one dimensional item would be a straight line because it has length, but no width. A three dimensional object is like a cone or a box or a pyramid because it has width and depth.

Let's talk about triangles in general. The first thing of importance about triangles is that every triangle has 180^0. If you add all three angles together they will always equal 180^2. It is obvious that the equilateral triangle has 180^0 because it has been labelled for you and you can add the three 60^0 angles and get 180^0. The right triangle only has a label at one angle and all you know about the acute triangle is that all angles are less than 90^0. You also only know that the obtuse angle has one angle greater than 90^0. However, all these triangles have a total of 180^0.

The formula for the area of a triangle is:

$$\frac{1}{2}\, b \cdot h,$$

where b is the base side we are working with and h is the height from the base that makes a 90 degree angle to that base.

The formula for finding a side to a right triangle is the Pythagorean Theorem and is:

$$c^2 = a^2 + b^2$$

where c is the hypotenuse (longest side) of a right triangle and a and b are the other two sides.

Right Triangles:

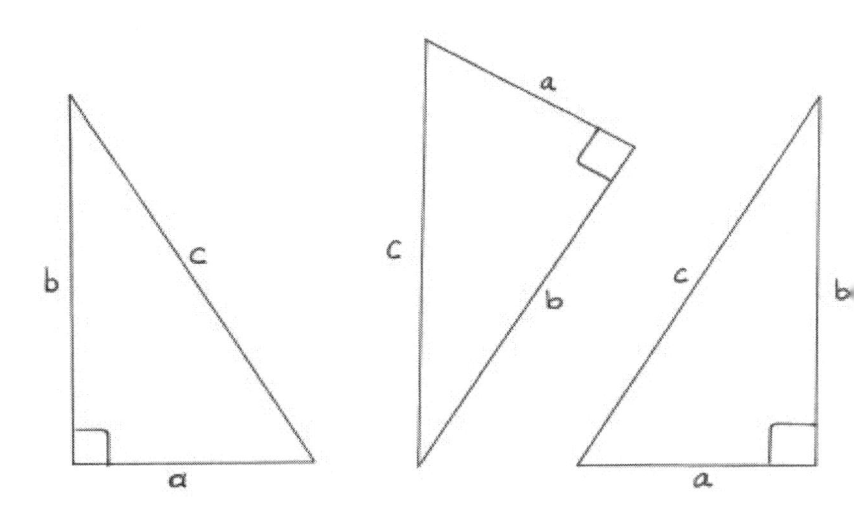

On tests and in math books, the right triangle may be shown in many different contortions with many different sized lengths. You must recognize that as long as it has a 90^0 angle, it is a right triangle. Whenever I had a test question involving a right triangle, I always drew it to where the 90^0 degree angle was to the left and on the bottom like the first drawing. It just seemed easier to work with.

Just to reacquaint you with your geometry, let's just do two problems.

<u>Problem 1:</u>

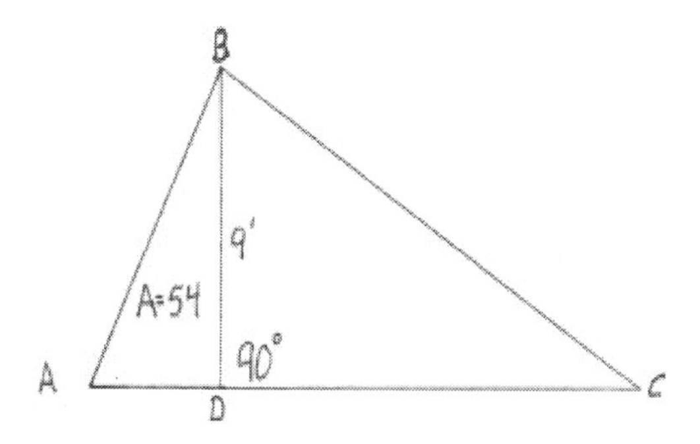

The isosceles triangle ABC shown has an area of 54 feet for right triangle ABD. Find the perimeter of DBC. The height (sometimes referred to as the altitude) is 9 feet. Line segment AC is 30 feet.

Solution:

They drew this one for us. However they did not write in the distance from A to C, but told us it was 30 feet. We should write this in ourselves. We can add the dimension of the sides as we determine them.

First, we note that angle ADB is also a right angle. We know this because we were told in our geometry book that the arc on any point on a line is 180^0. This is quite logical because if you took two right triangles and laid them back to back like the figure above the two 90^0 angles would add to 180^0.

So first let's solve for line segment AD.

Since Area = ½ Base x Height

54 = ½ AD x 9

½ AD = 6

AD = 12

Also by the Pythagorean Theorem we know that

The hypotenuse $(AB)^2 = 9^2 + 12^2$

$$(AB)^2 = 225$$

AB = 15 and DC = 18 (by subtracting 12 from 30

Let's add the numbers to the drawing to see where we are:

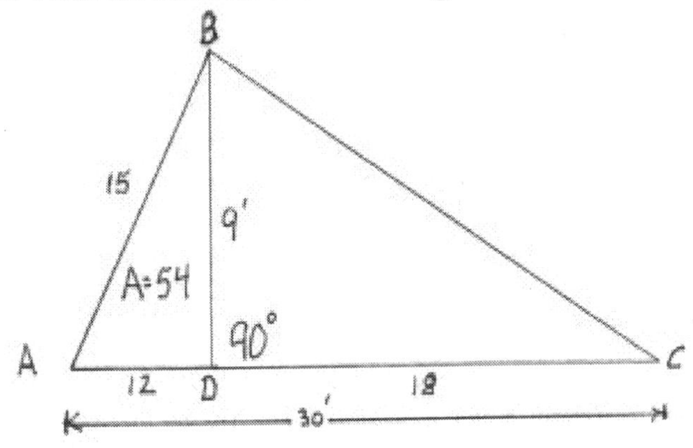

So we still need BC to obtain the perimeter of DBC

Using the Pythagorean Theorem,

$$(BC)^2 = 9^2 + 18^2$$

$$(BC)^2 = 81 + 324$$

$$BC = 20.1$$

So the perimeter of DBC = 9 + 20.1 + 18 = 47.1 feet.

Problem 2:
Line segment AB has a length of 10 feet. What is the perimeter and area of triangle ABC? Angle ABC is 60^0, angle BCA is 30^0.

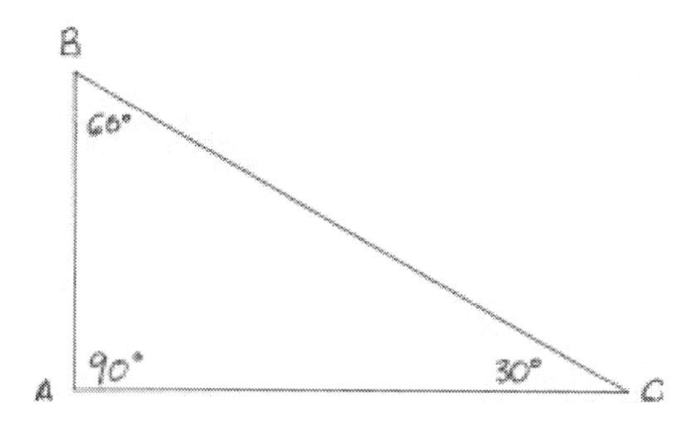

Solution:

Solving this problem, requires the definition of a 30-60-90 triangle. A 30-60-90 triangle always has the sides in the following ratio of lengths:

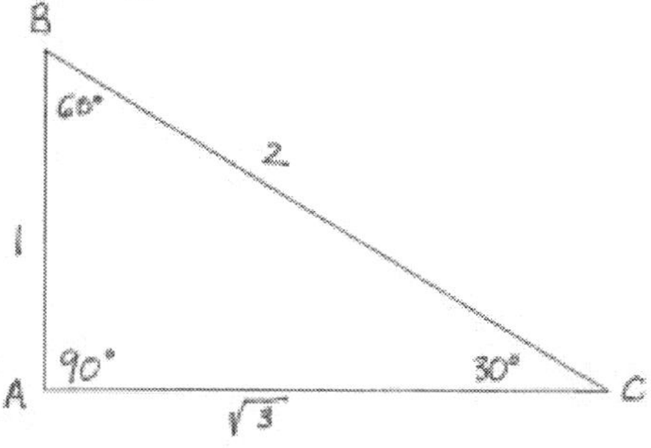

Thus side AB is 10 and therefore side BC is 20 feet.

Side AC is equal to $\sqrt{3} \times 10$

$\sqrt{3} = 1.732$

$1.733 \times 10 = 17.32$

Perimeter = 10 + 20 + 17.32 = 47.32 feet

Area = ½ 10 x 17.32

Area = 86.6 square feet (ft^2)

Rectangles:

The definition of a rectangle is that all angles are 90^0. A square is a rectangle in which all the sides are equal as well as all the angles being 90^0. Area of a rectangle is the length x width (L x W). The perimeter is 2L + 2W or 2(L + W).

Circles:

Circles are given by two formulas;

$$C = \pi d, \text{ where}$$

C = circumference (fancy word for perimeter
$\pi = 3.14$
d = diameter (line across the center of the circle connecting two points across from each other on the circumference of the circle)

And

$$A = \pi r^2 \text{, where}$$

A = area of the circle
$\pi = 3.14$ (sometimes given as 22/7)
r = radius (line from the center of the circle to any point on the circumference)

π is a symbol called Pi and pronounced just like in apple pie and is the ratio of the circumference of a circle to the diameter. No matter how big the diameter and thus the circle, this number of 3.14 for the ratio is always the same.

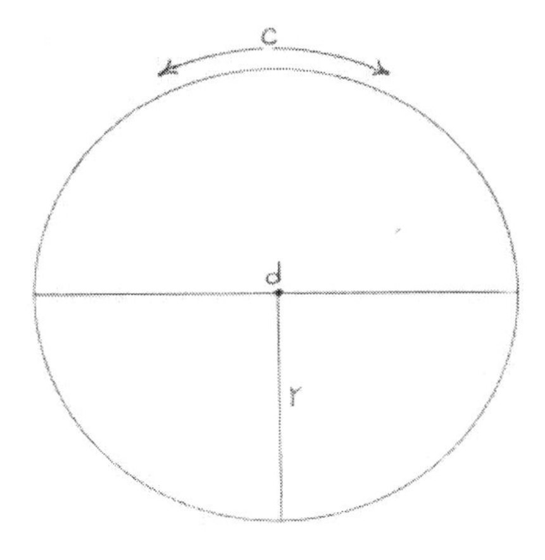

c = circumference (distance around like a perimeter for a rectangle)
d = diameter of the circle (the dot below the "d" is the center)
r = radius of the circle
c/d = π = 3.14   or 22/7

Note: **2r = d**

Sin, Cosine, and Tangent

Many times we do not have enough information to obtain the unknown side or angle of a right triangle. For this reason a relationship between the angles and the sides were developed by mathematicians many years ago.

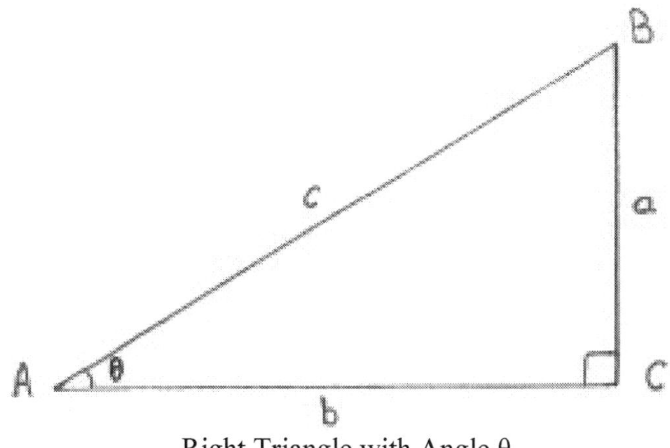

Right Triangle with Angle θ

For an angle opposite a side, the ratio of that side over the hypotenuse is equal to the sin of that angle. In the triangle above, sin $\theta = a/c$. There is a look up table for the sin θ of any angle. You can use a look up table in the back of your trigonometry book or on line by requesting a sin cosine table or just put the angel in with the word sin in front of it. Once you have this number and either the length of the hypotenuse or side a in the drawing you can find the other side.

Sin θ = opposite over hypotenuse

In the drawing it would be sin $\theta = a/c$

For an angle adjacent to a side, the ratio of that side over the hypotenuse is equal to the cosine of that angle. The same table that gives the sin also lists the cosine of any angle.

Cosine θ = adjacent over hypotenuse

In the drawing it would be cosine $\theta = b/c$

If you only have the length of one of the sides adjacent to the hypotenuse and want the length of the other side adjacent to the hypotenuse, you can use the ratio of the angle opposite either of these sides and it is equal to the tangent of that side in the following ratio:

Tangent θ = opposite/adjacent

Let's do a problem using the diagramed Right Triangle with Angle θ.

Problem 3:

In the triangle in the drawing we are told that side a is 12 feet in length and that angle θ is 29^0. What is the size of the hypotenuse and what is angle ABC?

Solution:

Always sketch the drawing before starting, put down what we know and what they are asking for.

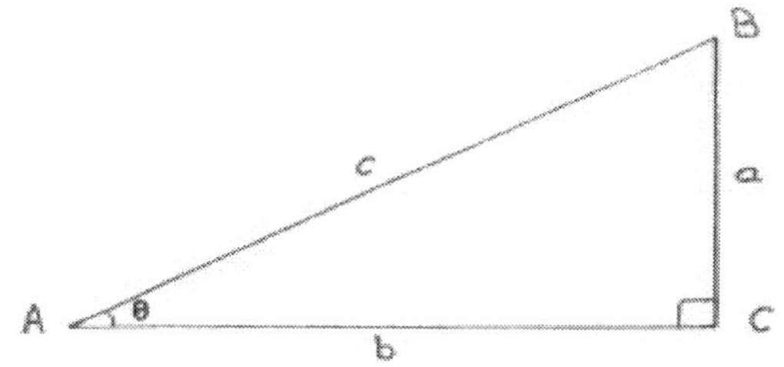

Side a = 12 ft.
Angle $\theta = 29^0$

Using sin θ

$\sin \theta = 12/c$

From the look up table:

$\sin \theta = 0.48481$

$0.48481 = 12/c$

$c = 24.75$ ft

Since the three sides of a triangle always = 180^0, ABC = 61^0

Problem 4:

Find the angles of a right triangle whose sides are 9 ft. and 12 ft.

Solution:

As always, make a sketch

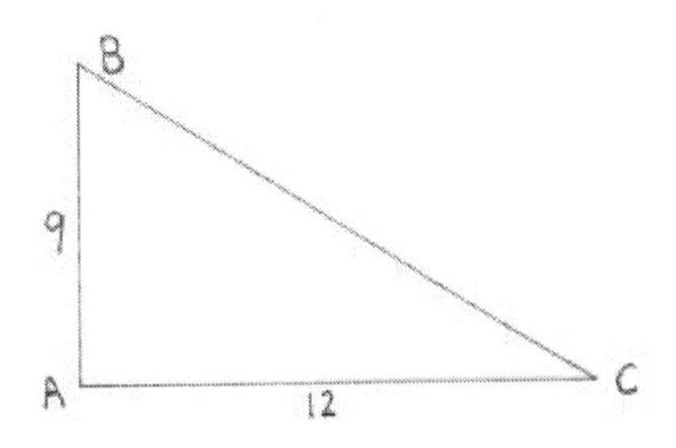

From the tangent function:

Tan θ = opposite/adjacent

Let's just do angle ABC first

Tan θ = opposite/adjacent = 12/9

Tan θ = 1.33333

Looking up tan 1.33333, we find

Tangent 1.32704 = 53^0
Tangent 1.37638 = 54^0

By interpolating

(1.37638-1.32704 = 0.0493/degree)

(1.37638-1.33333 = 0.04305)

.04305/.0493 = .87 of one degree less than 54^0

So angle ABC = 53.13 degrees

We know that this is a right triangle and all angles must add to 180^0

So angle BCA must be 36.87^0

Check:

Let's check it by using the tangent formula for angle BCA

$$\text{Tan BCA} = 9/12 = 0.75$$

Looking up tan 0.75, we find

$$\text{Tangent } 0.72654 = 36^0$$
$$\text{Tangent } 0.75355 = 37^0$$

By interpolating

Angle BCA = 36.87 and so it checks

Second check:

A final check would be to use the sin or cosine to obtain the length of the hypotenuse and then check to see if the Pythagorean Theorem holds.

Let's do the sine:

Sin = opposite over hypotenuse

$$\text{Sin ABC} = 12/c$$

$$\text{Sin of } 53.13 = 0.799999$$

So

$$c = 12/(0.799999) = 15\text{ft.}$$

From the Pythagorean theorem:

$$15^2 = 9^2 + 12^2$$

$$225 = 81 + 144$$

225 = 225 so it checks

Law of sines and cosines:

Not all triangles are right triangles. For those that are not there is the law of sines and cosines.

Law of sines:

The law of sines is a relationship that equates one side and its opposing angle to another side and its opposing angle. In a given triangle the following relationship holds:

$$\sin A/a = \sin B/b = \sin C/c$$

thus if you know only one side length and two angles you can obtain the other side or
if you know two sides and one angle you can find the other angle.

<u>Problem 5:</u>

You are given that you have a triangle in which $C = 60^0$, $a = 4$ feet and $b = 6$ feet. Find angle A.

Let's sketch the problem as follows:

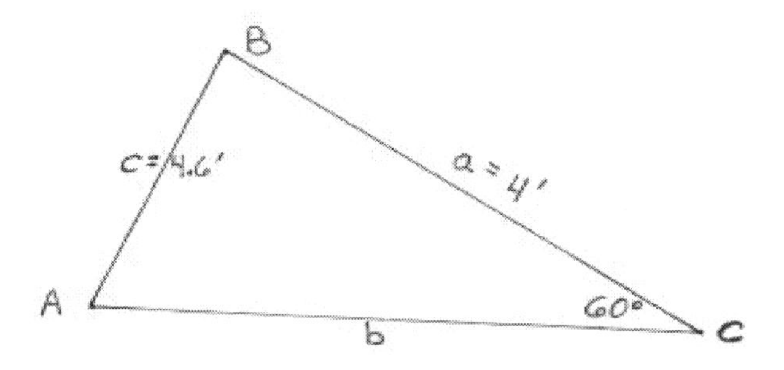

Solution:

Using law of sines

$$\sin A/4 = \sin 60^0/4.6$$

$$\sin A = (4 \text{ x } \sin 60^0)/4.6$$

$$\sin A = (4 \text{ x } 0.86603)/4.6$$

$\sin A = .75307 = 49^0$ rounded to nearest degree

Law of cosines:

Again this law like the law of sines is for triangles that do not have a 90 degree angle. It is similar to the Pythagorean theorem except that it has an added number that is a function of the cosine of the angle opposite the unknown side in a triangle with two known sides. The law of cosines is:

$$c^2 = a^2 + b^2 - 2ab\cos\theta$$

where θ = the angle between a and b whose sides are known. Side c is the unknown length.

Problem 6:

Triangle ABC has a 110 degree angle and the two adjacent sides are of lengths 10 ft. and 4 ft. What is the length of the third side?

Solution:

As always make a sketch and determine the formula to be used.

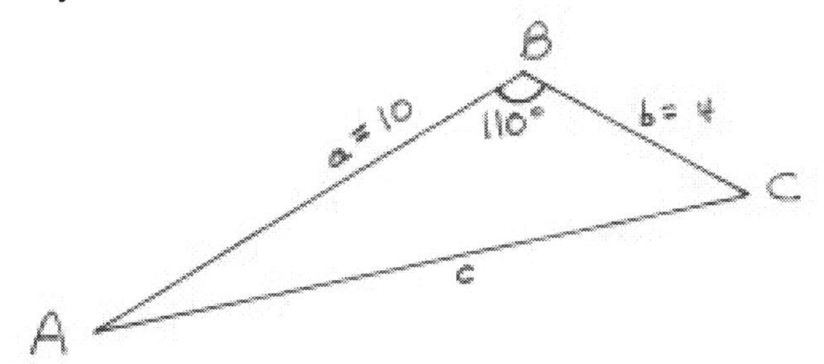

Find the length of side c.

Using the law of cosines

$$c^2 = a^2 + b^2 - 2ab\cos 110^0$$

Looking up the cosine of $110^0 = -0.342020124$

$$c^2 = 100 + 16 - 2\,(40)(-.34202)$$

$$c^2 = 116 + 27$$

$$c^2 = 143$$
$$c = 12$$

Exponents and logarithms:

The use of exponents makes work in math easier when working with very large or very small numbers. Multiplication of numbers like 900,000,000,000 or 0.000000000004356 are just too cumbersome.

The exponent for a base 10 system like that used throughout the world is as follows:

$$10^0 = 1$$
$$10^1 = 10$$
$$10^2 = 100$$
$$10^3 = 1{,}000$$
Etc.

Just know there are other base systems, such as base 2 and base 7. The exponent is the logarithm. Before we go onto logs let's just review math functions using exponents.

Addition of numbers with exponents. The rule is that you can only add numbers with the same exponent. So if you have $X^3 + 5X^3$ you can add these to 6 X^3. Subtraction is the same way.

When you multiply numbers with exponents you add the exponents.

$$X^3 \text{ x } X^2 = X^5$$

When you divide numbers with exponents, you subtract the exponents as follows:

$$X^6/X^4 = X^2$$

If it were $8X^6/2X^4$ then,

$$8X^6/2X^4 = 4X^2$$

Problem 7:

Demonstrate how $8X^5/4X^2 = 2X^3$ when X = 5 and the numbers are to the base 10.

Solution: Do the math and then check to show that it is a valid method.

$2X^3 = 2 \times (5x5x5) = 250$

Check:

$8X^5 = 8 \times (5x5x5x5x5) = 8 \times 3125 = 25{,}000$
$4X^2 = 4 \times (5 \times 5) = 4 \times 25 = 100$

Now divide 25,000 by 100 = 25,000

So it checks, but one can see that simply subtracting the exponents for division is much faster and less prone to errors.

What is a logarithm and how is it defined?

Our system of base 10 logarithms are called common logarithms. A logarithm is the exponent. Mathematicians took great pains to develop a relationship and table of the value of every exponent in a base system such that if you multiply by that number, it is the same as raising it to that power. Thus what do you have to multiply 10 by to get 10 raised to the third power. If you were to look it up in a log table or look on a calculator it would be 100. Thus if you multiply by the table reading for the third power you would see a number to the right that is the multiplier number or log. So the log of 3 is 100. Think of the 100 as the multiplier.

$$\text{Log}_b\, x = y \text{ if and only if } b^y = x$$

$$\log_{10} 1000 = 3, \text{ means } 10^3 = 1{,}000$$

thus the subscript after the word log is the base and the exponent is the number following the equal sign. There are other bases besides 10. There is base 2, base 7, and there is a base called the natural base. These are just some examples of other bases. We aren't going to cover natural logs, but you will learn more of these in trig class. For now we just want to give you a flavor of logarithms.

If you see a log written without a subscript (base), it is assumed that the subscript is 10.

Thus, $\log 100 = 2$ means $10^2 = 100$ thus we just have to know this means it is $\log_{10}$

Log table for base 10:

In working with logs, you can look up from a table or use a calculator. A typical log table would look like the following exert from a log table that went from 10^0 to 10^1. Only the first and last 10 log lookups are included from the table. Note $10^0 = 1$ and $10^1 = 10$ so it is obvious for the base 10 that the numbers in the right column are the values for the exponent itself. Thus $10^{1.01} = 0.004321$.

1.00	**0.000000**	....	9.91	**0.996074**
1.01	**0.004321**	....	9.92	**0.996512**
1.02	**0.008600**	....	9.93	**0.996949**
1.03	**0.012837**	....	9.94	**0.997386**
1.04	**0.017033**	....	9.95	**0.997823**
1.05	**0.021189**	....	9.96	**0.998259**
1.06	**0.025306**	....	9.97	**0.998695**
1.07	**0.029384**	....	9.98	**0.999131**
1.08	**0.033424**	....	9.99	**0.999566**
1.09	**0.037427**	....	10.00	**1.000000**
		....	100.00	**2.000000**

Exerts from Log table for base 10 using 6 figures beyond the decimal.

Let's do a simple one to show what we are talking about.

Problem 8:

Find $\log_{10} 100$.
Solution:

First we know that the base is 10. We then have to look up 100.

From the exert from the Log table chart $\log_{10} 100$ is 2.

$$\text{Log}_{10} = 2$$

Problem 9:

Write $4^3 = 64$ in logarithmic form.

Solution:

From the definition 4 is the base so $\log_4$. We know 3 is the exponent. So $\log_4 64 = 3$

Just remember the definition.

One last thing… $\log_b x^y = y \log_b x$

Problem 10:

Find the logarithm for 3^2.

Solution:

$$\log_b x^y = y \log_b x$$

Now we stated it above, let's demonstrate it:

Writing 3^2 in logarithmic form,

$$\text{Log}_{10} 3^2 = 2 \log_{10} 3$$

Looking up $\log_{10} 3$ we find it is .477121

So $2 \times .477121 = .954242$

Now let's look at the left side of the equation

We know that $3^2 = 9$

So from the look up table or calculator

$Log_{10}9 = 0.954242$

So the identity holds

So what do logarithms do for you?

Well, the reason for logarithms isn't something that you will likely use in your everyday life like algebra and geometry. The reason for logarithms was to solve problems that were not readily or easily solved with algebra. For example if you are a research computer programmer you are definitely using logarithms because all code is binary, either true or false. This means instead of a base 10 we have to use a base 2 for all our math functions in machine language because it is binary code. Sophisticated code is written on top of binary, but its origin in machine language is still $\log_2$ rather than $\log_{10}$.

For scientists and true mathematicians it is important because not everything works out neatly like problems 8 through 10. The next problem will demonstrate the need for logarithms.

Problem 11:

Find the value of **$2 \times 10^{1.08}$.**

Solution:

From the look up table we find $10^{1.08} = 0.033424$

Thus **$2 \times 0.033424 = .066848$**

Since we know that $10^1 = 0$ we would expect this to be a low number and it is.

Radians:

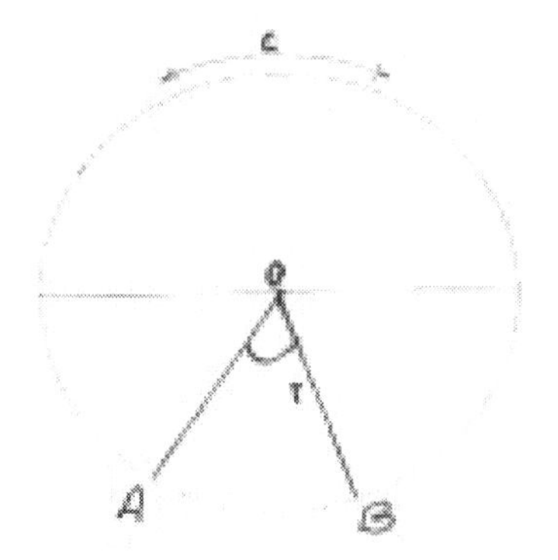

A radian is the angle that creates the pie shaped piece that is cut by any two radius segments. In the drawing these are represented by lines AO and BO. The side BO is labeled r. The arc of the radian is determined by the angle between the two sides.

By definition: When the length of arc AB is equal in length to the radius this is called a radian. The angle of the arc is represented by the term rad. So that AB rad would be the angle cut by the arc AB of the circle. The size of the angle for one radian is approximately 57.2958^0. The size of the angle is given by the formula:

$$1 \text{ rad} = 1 \times 180^0/\pi \approx 57.2958^0 \text{ or } 1 \text{ rad} = 180^0/\pi$$

As stated, one radian is equal to $180/\pi$ degrees. Thus, to convert from radians to degrees, multiply by $180/\pi$.

Problem 12:

How many radians in a circle? Express in terms of π.

Since 1 radian = $180^0/\pi$

You can multiply both sides by π

1π radian = 180^0

Multiply both sides by 2

$2\ \pi$ radians = 360^0

Mathematicians use radians because they work out more elegantly than regular degrees. Since a circle is exactly $2\ \pi$ radians, then a straight line would be $1\ \pi$ radian. Thus a 90 degree angle in a rectangle would be exactly $2\pi/4$ radians or $1/2\ \pi$ rad and so on for any angle.

Equation of a line:

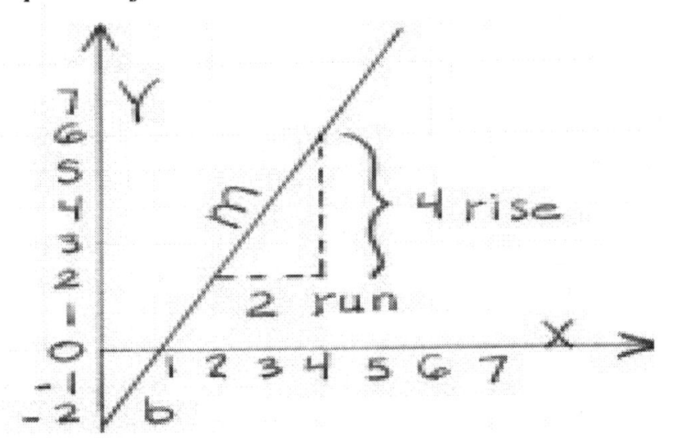

The slope of a line is the rise over the run or in this case m = 4/2 =r 2.

The equation for a line is:

$y = mx + b$ where,

y = vertical axis point or coordinate value
x = horizontal axis point or coordinate value
m = slope (rise/run)
b = y intercept (where the line crosses the y axis)

This equation describes exactly where the line is in a two dimensional space. It is also the definition of a line.

A point on a graph is always given in coordinates of x and y and is always (x,y). If you know 2 points you can know where the line is and thus the slope and also where the y intercept (b) is. This of course assumes that it is a straight line.

Problem 13:

If you are given two points (0,-2) and (6,4) and if the line these points fall on is a straight line draw the line and determine the slope.

Solution:

The graph of the line would be the first thing to do since that is what they asked for first. The slope can be determined two ways.

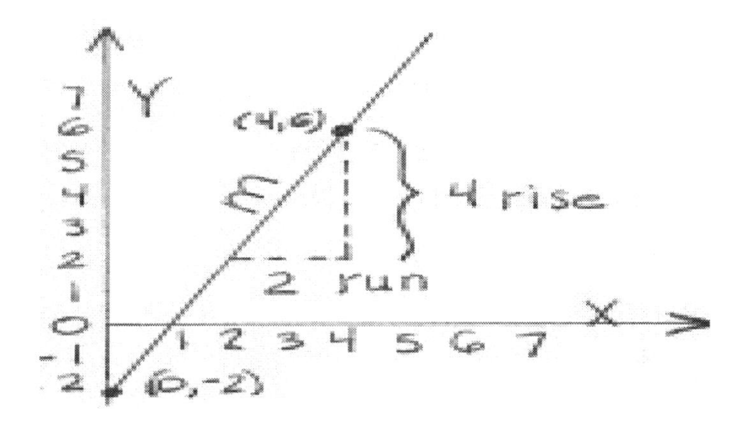

The slope is clear from the rise over the run

m = 4/2 = 2

Another way to do the slope is to remember the formula for m

$m = (y_1 - y_2)/(x_1 - x_2)$ x and y being any two points on the line

Thus using the point given to us we would not have had to graph the line to determine m

$m = (6- -2)/(4-0) = 8/4 = 2$

m = 2

Problem 14:

Determine the equation of the line with slope 3 that passes through (2,1).

Solution:

We could graph it, but we could also use a little algebra as follows:

Let (x,y) be a point on the line.

Then $m = 3 = (y-1)/(x-2)$

Transposing

$$3\,(x-2) = y-1$$

$$3x - 6 = y-1$$

$$\underline{\mathbf{y = 3x - 5}}$$

Summary:

You now have a basic understanding of Trigonometry. You know what it is going to look like because you have now seen the Reader's Digest version that is the short version for the course. Some of the examples shown to you were on a high level and some on a simple level. School will fill in the spaces between the simple and complex.

With practice, problem solving will become second nature. This overview will give you a leg up on doing well in trigonometry. The biggest thing is practice, practice, practice. Just like in real estate it is location, location, location. The methods and techniques described in this book will net you an A if followed.

Remember, it's important to know how to use the equations. I have never seen a test in which a student was asked to derive a formula or equation. If you go into higher math this may be valuable, but it is not necessary now. Remember, it isn't how to build an engine, it's how to drive the car and knowing the rules of the road. This is not to say it isn't good to know where they came from, but a test is no time to try to remember how the equation was developed. You need to know what formula to use and how to apply it.

Also, don't think because you were not good in math in the past that you are going to be poor in trigonometry. This is definitely not the case. You could have been mediocre in math in the past and very well become an A student in trigonometry. While it does use knowledge from algebra and geometry if you use my methodology and techniques it's a whole new ball game.

Remember, this country needs more of you to go into math and science. It's where the jobs are going to be created. It's where the world can be made a better place and it's where the United States can stand tall amongst the other nations.

Best of luck and success to you,

John D. Forlini

Appendix A

Steps to Solve Word Problems:

1. First and foremost figure out what the problem wants from you. Sounds simple, but half the time this is where we fall down. Are they asking you for speed, numbers of kittens, or time. Whatever it is write it down and then give it a letter. For some reason most people like to use X. However, it is a great practice to use the letter that corresponds to what you are looking for.
2. Write down what units the answer should be in. Is it feet, square feet, or cubic feet, etc.
3. Ignore the unnecessary stuff in the word problem. Don't let stuff that is not essential confuse you.
4. If possible draw a picture that is representative of the question. Trigonometry questions lend themselves well to pictures and graphs.
5. Make a label (letter or number if given) for each item or variable.
6. Set up an equation or equations that satisfy the request and given information. Sometimes just putting the problems words into an equation will give you the guidance to solve the problem as will a good drawing.
7. Put the equation or equations into its simple easy form. Put all the letters on one side and the numbers on the other. If it's more than one equation, try to manipulate them to look alike. Sometimes this will mean that you don't have all the letters on one side and all the numbers on the right. You will have to play with it.
8. You will always hit that awful problem that you just can't see how to do. Don't waste time on this one, go to the next one. Remember on an ACT entrance exam or other exam most of the time every problem has equal weight. So put this one aside for later. The brain is an amazing thing. Sometimes while you are working on other problems, your brain will be unconsciously working out the solution to the problem.
9. Check your work quickly by substituting your answer back into the original equation.
10. Finally, look at your answer and ask if it makes sense.

CHAPTER 7 CALCULUS

FIRST: If you haven't already done so, go back and read the section on "The purpose of this book" and "The Introductory Overview" before you start. Most important, if you are a student, go back and read Chapter 2 " For Students". It's only 2 pages.

So **what** ***is calculus really?***

Calculus is the ultimate math for students. It is an extension of algebra, geometry, and trigonometry. It is the study of rates of change and expansion from linear to volumetric from one dimension to three dimension. For instance, it can take a line and determine the area under that line through formula. Calculus is divided into two disciplines—differential calculus whose equations handle rate changes and integral calculus that handles expansion. Differential calculus (also referred to as derivative calculus) and integral calculus are mathematically related.

Differential and integral calculus formulas:

As part of an overview, I am going to show the core formulas that will be used over and over in different forms for these two halves of calculus and explain how they are related. This is the core of the course.

Differential calculus core formula also called the power rule:

If $f(x) = x^k$ with $k \neq -1$, then $f'(x) = k(x^{k-1})$

This formula in differential calculus is called the derivative. Mathematicians will use the term differentiate and take the derivative interchangeably.

Integral calculus core formula:

If $f'(x) = x^k$ with $k \neq -1$, then $f(x) = x^{k+1}/(k + 1) + C$
The constant C will drop out when you go from $x = n$ to $x = n'$ because $C-C = 0$

At this point this doesn't have any meaning to you so let's explain using a real life problem.

Problem 1:

Develop a formula for the area under the curve (line) that is drawn in the diagram. Determine the area that is shaded using this formula. The x and y axis are measured in feet.

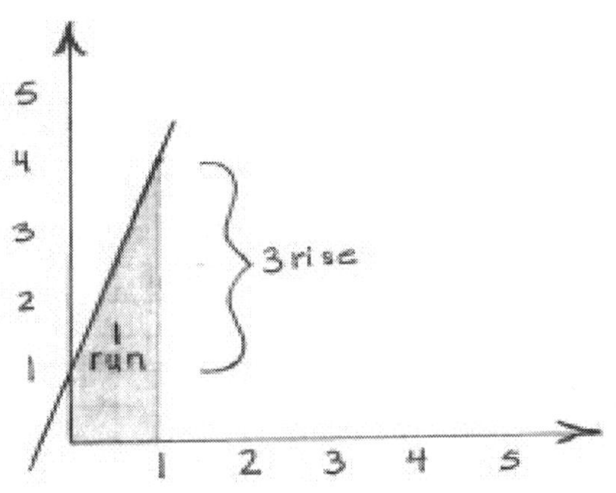

Solution:

Normally the rise and run would not have been drawn in for the student, but to remind one of the trigonometry of the equation of a line this has been put in as an aid. Also, you have not really been given enough information to solve this problem yet. If we had stated that the area under a curve could be obtained by taking the integral of the equation of that curve between two points that might have helped. We will leave it at that for now for this simple problem.

First, develop the equation for the line that is described

$$y = mx + b$$

$$y = 3x + 1$$

we could also write this as a function of x

$$f(x) = 3x + 1$$

taking the integral of this formula from the integral formula

$$3x^2/2 + x$$

Substituting for x = 1

$$3\,(1^2)/2 + 1 = \text{area of shaded portion under the line}$$

$$= \mathbf{2.5}\ \text{ft.}^2$$

Now remember I said that I would show how differential calculus and integral calculus were related. Well if we now take the differential (derivative) of the area formula of ($f(x) = 3x^2/2 + x$) we get:

$$3x + 1$$

This is important so make sure you understand that you took the differential equation of $3x^2/2 + x$ and multiplied $3x^2/2$ by two and reduced the exponent by one. You multiplied the x by 1 and then reduced the exponent from 1 to zero. Remember x^0 is equal to one and thus it became $3x + 1$ using the differential equation. We will explain more as we go, but just know the mechanics for now and the relationship between integral and derivative.

So the differential and the integral are related and can be converted one to the other. This is oversimplified and relative in this problem. There is a constant involved in other cases, but since the area was from 0 to one there was no issue with the constant. This this will be explained further later.

This is the core of calculus, but I have taken some liberties in conventions and over simplified it. Had I showed this with proper calculus nomenclature it would have looked like this for the integral:

$$\int_0^1 (3x + 1)dx = 3x^2/2 + 1] = (3\cdot 1^2/2 + 1) - (3\cdot 0^2/2 + 0) = 5/2 = 2.5$$

I didn't want to scare you right away so I simplified the convention for this one basic problem that allowed this simplification. However, when we now go to ground zero you will have an idea what it's all about. And when you get into class armed with what you are going to read in the rest of this condensed calculus treatise and methodology you will be on the path towards an A in calculus. It won't be easy, but it will be a great deal easier having a solid familiarity along with the technique that I will share as follows:

1. First, get a notebook that is bound. One that you will not lose the pages.
2. Take notes on one side of the page, leaving the other blank. You can take your notes on the right side or the left depending on which is easier for you. I always used the left side.
3. Purchase a good red marking pen.
4. As quickly after class as possible fix your illegible notes. I used to stay in the seat for 5 minutes before running to the next class. I would use my red pen to mark my notes so I could decipher them later on. When you are hurrying to take notes sometimes what seems clear when you are writing cannot be understood when you get home. But it is most likely still fresh in your mind right after class so now you can write over an illegible word or symbol in red to make it clear for later. If you wait too long you will wonder what the heck you wrote.
5. Before you start any other homework from other subjects copy your calculus notes from one side of the page to the other. This reinforces what you have learned in class and makes it much neater. By having both pages side by side you can always refer to the original if you copied wrong. I always gave myself a treat when I started doing the copying. When I sat down to do calculus I had a coke and a candy bar. It was my special time. Now at my age a coke and a candy bar would give me heartburn, but I was younger then. I did the same thing with my other math courses.
6. After you have copied your notes, then do your calculus homework problems. **DO THEM ALL.** Don't be lulled into false security because they seem redundant. Some may be redundant and some may have just a slight trick to them that you would not have caught if you skipped the problem.

7. Check your answers. If you got it wrong, fix it and highlight it in yellow. If you can't figure it out and have struggled with it, then the next day in class the light will shine when your teacher goes over it. But do your best to struggle if necessary to figure it out. And if you don't understand it after the teacher explains it, ask him or her to further explain.
8. Highlight the problems that you missed.
9. Redo the highlighted problems that you missed first time.
10. Write down in red on the problem itself any questions you might have so you can ask them in class.
11. Now you are ready for class.
12. The teacher will likely go over homework and then present new material. If you have done everything above, you will find that it is just refreshing to go over the homework problems that you have already done.
13. Don't get cocky.
14. When you study for your test do practice problems from your homework, especially the ones that were highlighted in yellow. If you miss one, mark it in some way and do it again before the test.
15. This next item can very well make the difference between a B and an A. Many teachers will give students their test back. So if you can find someone from the previous year who still has their tests, get their test and make sure you can do every problem on it. The teacher will not give the same test to you, but knowing how to do the previous year's test is a great way to help know what the teacher considers important. It is a great learning tool. Don't shirk on this one. Find someone who has taken these tests.
16. Smile when your paper comes back with a nice high mark. Because if you follow the above this is what is going to happen.
17. When you do well be prepared for your friends and peers to give you a hard time. Just tell them you find calculus fun just like a video game. That should shut them up. Don't let them discourage you or make you feel bad for doing well. Just know that they are jealous and would never admit it. Ten years from now when you have the nice home, the great car and boat, and the great

significant other, what they think now will be totally insignificant and meaningless.

18. One last thing–Don't miss one class. You can catch up in history or English, but calculus is tough. It's probably 10 times harder than history to catch up. If you have to be out sick, try to come in for the calculus class and then go back home. Your parents can write you a note. If you are in sports, try to fix your schedule to take calculus in the morning so that you are not pulled out at the end of the day for a game or game practice. Some schools like to have special programs where a student leaves class for something. Don't get talked into skipping out on calculus.
19. If your teacher is available for help after hours take full advantage of this. For some reason students in high school seem to avoid this teacher help. Maybe you have to ride the bus or his or her times for help are not good, but if the teacher does make time available for help take full advantage of it. You are crazy not to, especially if you want an A.

    Some teachers take email. This is a great way to work with your teacher. Some teachers are great and some aren't. Remember their job is to help you. Don't be bashful about getting help. Also, the internet is a great source of help. If you have a question, type it in in google. Sometimes the internet explains things better than the teacher. However, the teacher should be primary because he or she makes up the test and knows what is important.
20. One last thing. Occasionally, you will get a teacher who works directly off the book and has you turn to the page in the book and reads off the page and explains the course from the page itself. This makes it hard to do the notebook routine.

    In this case, I recommend using a pencil and writing your notes of explanation in the book margins so that you can understand it later when you study from these pages. You may end up paying a fine for doing this, but it would be worth it and you would probably be doing the next student a favor by writing good notes in the margin.

You should still look over your notes in the margins as soon as possible, like right after the class, just like the notebook. You can then write your notes in a notebook when you get home or just reread the ones on the margin of the book. Again, do the problems. Keep a notebook for these problems so that you will always have them organized. Mark the ones you have trouble with and do these over again until you are totally comfortable with them.

Let's do two more problems so we get the mechanics down and then we will start from the beginning and provide the basis for conventions and include more problems as we go so you will have a basic understanding and appreciation for what calculus is about before you hit that first day of class.

However, before we leave problem 1 let's find that same area using plain old trigonometry and geometry. We'll call it problem 2.

Problem 2 Using the sketch below find the area of the lightly shaded portion on the right side of the y axis. The x and y axis are measured in feet.

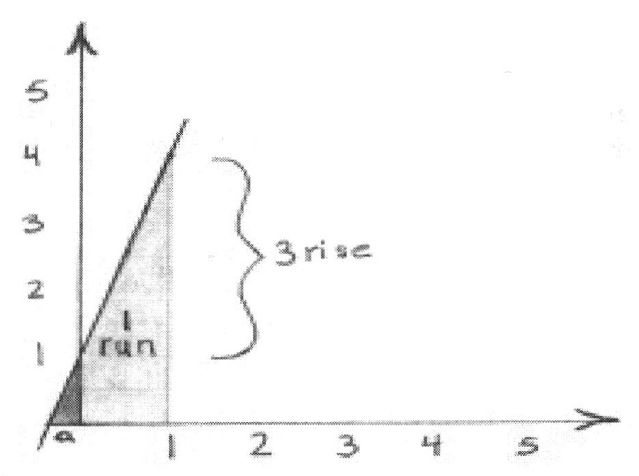

Solution:

It's obvious that we now have two triangles, the large one shaded with both light shade and dark shade and the smaller one that is dark shaded only. To find the area of the lightly shaded piece to the right of the y axis would involve subtracting the small triangle from the large one. All we need is that small side of the dark triangle labelled (a).

We know that a goes from right to left starting at (0,0). We know the slope is 3 so if we call the left side of a point (a,y) then the equation of the line would be $y = 3a + 1$

We know that $y = 0$ so

$$0 = 3a + 1$$

$$a = 1/3 \text{ ft.}$$

So we now know that the bottom leg of the larger triangle is thus:

$$1/3 + 1 = 4/3$$

Since the area of a triangle is ½ b·h, then the big triangle is:

$$\tfrac{1}{2}(4/3) \times 4 = 8/3$$

And the small triangle is:

$$\tfrac{1}{2}(1/3) \times 1 = 1/6$$

So $8/3 - 1/6 = 16/6 - 1/6 = 15/6 = 5/2 =$ **2.5 ft.²**

And so our calculus method checks with plane old trigonometry and geometry.

But it was a lot easier to use calculus, wasn't it!

Okay, so now that you are a believer in the value of calculus, let's do two more problems to get the mechanics down before going into the conventions and applications of calculus.

Problem 3:

Find the derivative of $x^4 + 4x^2$ using the derivative formula.

Note: (We could have said differentiate $x^4 + 4x^2$)

Solution:

Using the formula for derivative:

$kx^{\mathbf{k-1}}$

$\mathbf{4x^3 + 2x}$

Problem 4:

Find the integral of $10^4 + 6x^2 + 2x - 4$ using the integral formula.

Solution:

Using the integral formula:

$x^{k+1}/(k + 1) + C$

$\mathbf{2x^5 + 2x^3 + x^2 - 4x + C}$

Note: One of the rules not yet given is that for a number or letter by itself you just add an x after the number or letter. There are more rules to come, but for now you have the basic mechanics.

Objective of this section of the book on calculus.

There is only one objective to this section of the book. That is to provide you with the insight and the methods and techniques to get on the path to get an A in calculus.

What you do now will make all the difference when you sit down on your first day of calculus class in your high school. This book is designed to provide just the right amount of material to keep the student's attention without overwhelming him or her with too much material.

The ideal time to read this material and practice the problems and solutions is the summer before you take the course. It is also best to read and study this material in short intervals, perhaps a half hour at a time. Do the presented problems over and over. There are only 17, but they are comprehensive so that if you can do these you will be more than prepared for that first day. After you have seen the solution to a problem, come back to the problem the next day and try to do it without looking at the solution. The more you do this the more it will sink in and the greater your chance of an A in the course.

Things You Need to Know Before You Even Start.

Calculus is not something that sinks in from the start. It is complex and it uses everything you have learned in algebra, geometry, and trigonometry. A good teacher is invaluable. If your teacher is mediocre it's going to be tough. I had a good dedicated teacher in college. About half way through my first semester of calculus I realized it was too complicated and I just wasn't getting it even though I was doing okay on tests. So I went to see the teacher one afternoon in his office. We went to a classroom to use the blackboards because he could tell it wasn't going to be easy to get the concept across.

Two hours later with all the blackboards filled, I finally caught on and did well from then on. I therefore know you will not grasp the total concept of calculus from this one book. My hope is that I can give you a "flavor" of what it is about without scaring you to death. My advice to you is to consider seriously if you even want to take this course. Talk to your advisor, think about what your goals are, and if possible take the course in the summertime before you have to take it in your high school. If you do well then you can transfer the credit and enjoy your senior year. If you did mediocre and think that you are ready to take the course at your school to get a high mark, then don't transfer the credit, but take the course and get that A.

Or decide that you have had enough math for now and that you want to concentrate on getting A's in your other courses like physics. Chances are if you are thinking about taking calculus you are going to be a senior and you will also be taking physics. Taking physics and calculus at the same time could be too much for you. It would be better to get an A in physics than to get C's in both physics and calculus.

I opted to take physics and no math in my senior year. I did get an A in physics and had a wonderful senior year. I even won an award in a science fair for a physics project. So it might be better to decide what your goals are and then make an intelligent decision. Not taking calculus will not negatively impact your goal to go on with science and math or any technical endeavor that you choose. In fact, it might be a blessing to do well in the other subjects and concentrate on getting good marks on the SAT or ACT. Hopefully, you have a good guidance counselor.

Plus if you are not planning to go to college, but take advantage of the industrial technical opportunities, then calculus is not going to be necessary. It would be far better to do well in the 5 previous courses in this book than to pull your average down with calculus. I know this may sounds like heresy, but I would rather you left high school with a positive outlook than feel defeated because of calculus. If you go on to college and decide to major in a science or math career or go for an engineering degree and you did not take calculus so that you could concentrate on grades and ACT and SAT scores, then it would be a smart idea to take calculus in the summer before college. This way you can devote your time to this one course.

Ground zero

Ground zero starts with understanding the concept of limit and how it applies to the development of calculus. We will introduce limit at this point and then do some problems and then towards the end show the derivation of the derivative formula that we have given you and how the concept of limits leads to the formula for derivative.

As an example, the limit is written:

$$\lim_{x \to k} f(x) = L$$

and is read "The limit of f(x) as x goes to k is L". Thus some function of x becomes L the closer it gets.

Let's look at one.

$$\lim_{x \to 3} 2x$$

If we approach it from x greater than 3 then:

$$x = 3.100 \text{ then } 2x = 6.200$$
$$x = 3.001 \text{ then } 2x = 6.002$$

If we approach it from x less than 3 then:

$x = 2.900$ then $2x = 5.800$
$x = 2.999$ then $2x = 5.998$

It certainly looks like the closer we get to $x=3$ the closer $2x$ becomes 6.

We can say from this effort that:

$$\lim_{x \to k} f(x) = 6$$

where the $f(x) = 2x$

Okay, so why are we doing this. Obviously, $f(x) = 2x$ for 3 is going to be 6.

But what if we had the following:

$$\lim_{x \to 2} x\text{-}2/x\text{-}2$$

We can see that this would normally be 0/0, which is an indeterminate number.

However, if we approach it from x greater than 2 then:

$x = 2.100$ then $(2\text{-}2.1 \,/\, 2\text{-}2.1) = (\text{-}.1/\text{-}.1) = 1$

It would be the same if we approached 2 from less than 2. It would always be 1.

$$\lim_{x \to 2} f(x) = 1$$

where the $f(x) = x\text{-}2/x\text{-}2$

which reads "as the limit of x goes to 2, but is not actually 2 but infinitesimally close to 2, the equation $(x\text{-}2/x\text{-}2)$ equals one."

Okay, hold this thought and nomenclature as we move on to the definition of derivative and do some problems. We will eventually explain this more definitively when we derive the formula that you will be using. Most books in calculus start off developing the formula. We will develop it as well, but not right away.

The derivative:

We have already introduced the derivative as half of the calculus course. The derivative is defined and explained in different ways. It can be thought of as the slope of a curve at a single point or the tangent line. It can also be the instantaneous rate of change. If a rocket ship is hurtling towards outer space and you needed the instantaneous velocity at some time (t) then you would use derivative calculus.

I personally like looking at it as an instantaneous rate of change. Supposing you look at the formula for average velocity. This formula $\Delta v/\Delta t$ says that the change in v (velocity) over the time interval Δt is some number. It gives the average velocity over some time period. Say you are driving and attempting to hold your speed at 60 mph. Well at times you may be going 58 or 62 but over time you would average 60. Even your cruise control will do this. If you are accelerating, your velocity will be changing and thus an instantaneous velocity at time t will be different than at time $t + n$.

Suppose we wanted to find a change in the position as the change in time approaches 0. You could write this as lim $\Delta x/ \Delta t$ normally, but for an infinitesimal difference we would write $\Delta x/ \Delta t$ instead as dx/dt as x approaches zero ($x \rightarrow 0$).

Going back to graphic analysis like tangent, we can define the x and y coordinates as dy/dx. The dy/dx is then the graph of $y = f(x)$. Obviously, this relationship depends on x so we therefore think of it as a function of x. The process of computing dy/dx is called differentiation or derivative calculus. Differentiation then results in the derivative of the original function that defines the value of any x as the slope at x.

The actual mathematical definition of derivative is:

Let f(x) be a function. Then $f'(x) = \left(\lim_{\Delta x \rightarrow 0} f(x + \Delta x) - f(x)\right) / \Delta x$

If this limit exists then f is differentiable and its derivative at x is $f'(x)$.

I really don't expect you to grasp this yet, but be aware of it. I have looked at many full blown explanations. For now know the formula and do the problems. We will come back to this concept of limit and how it is used to derive the derivative. First, though we need to provide some nomenclature and rules.

Nomenclature

$f^{/}(x)$ read f prime of x. It is for the derivative of f(x).

dy/dx is for the derivative of y as a function of x as well.

Sometimes the derivative is notated as $y^{/}$.

Thus $y^{/} = dy/dx = f^{/}(x)$. Thus you may be asked to perform the derivative in several different ways.

$\int$ is the symbol for integral. When there is a value at the bottom and top it means take the integral from those two points and subtract the bottom integral from the top to obtain the integral or summation between those two points. This is put here under derivatives section so as not to confuse the integral and the derivative notations. We will cover this more when we come to integrals.

Some Rules for derivative

1. If $f'(x) = x^k$ then $f(x) = k(x^{k-1})$ for positive integers. This is the formula for derivative. This formula is the simplified version of the one shown using Δx. We will show how this simplified version was developed from the other one later in this section.
2. Antiderivative for our purposes is the integral. However, there is a subtle difference. We'll cover integrals later.
3. The derivative of a constant is 0.
4. The derivative of a number or letter by itself is 0.
5. The derivative of x in a function of x without a power is 1.
6. Derivative of sin x = cosine x
7. Derivative of cosine x = - sin x

Let's do some problems. Every problem is a teacher in itself. Even if you don't understand the basics of calculus doing problems will eventually help your overall understanding. It will strengthen your skills such that when you see a problem on a test you will just automatically know what to do. Then after you have done some problems I will go back to the derivation of derivative and how the two formulas presented are really the same thing. Most text books start off with the development of the derivative, but I felt it was best to get some practical experience first..

Problem 5:

What is f' if $f(x) = x^6 + x^5 + x^4 + x^3 + x^2 + x + 5$

Solution:

$$f'(x)= 6x^5 + 5x^4 + 4x^3 + 3x^2 + 2x + 1 + 0$$

This is just to cement the mechanics. The next problem is for the same reason.
Note: Although we showed the 0, it is not necessary to show.

Problem 6:

What is f' if $f(x) = 10x^5 + 8x^4 + 6x^3 + 7x^2 + 5x - 8$

Solution:

$$50x^4 + 32x^3 + 18x^2 + 14x + 5 - 0$$

Note: Although we showed -0, it is not necessary to show this.

Problem 7:

Find $f'(x)$ for $5x^2 + 5x - 7$

Solution:

$2(5x) + 1(5) - 0(7) = 10x + 5$

Note: The 7 above is considered to be $7x^0$ thus 0 times 7 would be zero using the derivative formula. Or just remember the rule. The derivative of a number or constant is always zero.

Problem 8:

Differentiate with respect to x: $y = 7x^3$

Solution:

$$dy/dx = (3 \cdot 7)x^{3-1}$$

$$dy/dx = 21\ x^2$$

Problem 9:

Differentiate with respect to t: $y = 1/\sqrt{t^1}$

Solution:

$$y = 1/\sqrt{t^1}$$

from algebra

$$y = t^{-1/2}$$

$$dy/dx = -1/2t^{-3/2}$$

Problem 10:

Find dy/dx of $f(x) = 3x + 5$ and explain what that is.

$dy/dx = (3)(1)x^{1-1} = 3$ thus $dy/dx = 3$ is the slope at a point or the tangent at that point. By definition, the change in y over the change in x is the slope of a line.

Rules for integral calculus:

The integral is the expansion of the derivative.

1. If the derivative is $f'(x)$ (sometimes written as y') then $f(x)$ (the integral) is;

$$f(x) = (x^{k+1})/(k + 1) + C$$

2. The integral is denoted by $\int$.

$\int_0^5$ would mean the integral from 0 to 5

3. When taking an integral from one point to another, the constant C drops out because you are subtracting the integral at the bottom from the integral at the top of the integral sign.

4. $\int_a^b f(x)dx = F(b) - F(a)$ means the integral of the function $f(x)$ from a to b. It could be the area under a curve from point a to point b.

Problem 11:

If $y' = x^6 + x^5 + x^4 + x^3 + x^2 + x + 7$ find y.

Taking the integral,

$$y = x^7/7 + x^6/6 + x^5/5 + x^4/4 + x^3/3 + x^2/2 + x^1/1 + C$$

Obviously, $x^1/1 = x$ and would be written this way. It was shown this way just for clarity.

Problem 12:

If $y' = 14x^6 + 18x^5 + 10x^4 + 16x^3 + 9x^2 + 5x + 7$ find y.

Solution:

Taking the integral,

$$y = 2x^7 + 3x^6 + 2x^5 + 4x^4 + 3x^3 + 2.5x^2 + 7x + C$$

Problem 13:

If $y' = 4x^3$ find the integral from 2 to 4.

Solution

$$\int_a^b f(x)dx = F(b) - F(a)$$

Substituting:

$$\int_2^4 f(x)dx = F(4) - F(2)$$

$$F(x) = x^4 + C$$

$$F(4) = (4)^4 + C$$

$$F(4) = 256 + C$$

$$F(2) = (2)^4 + C$$

$$F(2) = 16 + C$$

Thus

$$\int_2^4 f(x)dx = F(4) - F(2)$$

$$= (256 + C) - (16 + C)$$

$$= 240$$

Problem 14:

If $y' = 4x^2 + 8x$ and $x = 3$ when $y = 10$, what is the equation for y.

First take the integral of y' which is y.

$$y = (4x^3)/3 + (8x^2)/2 + C$$

Then putting in the numbers for x and y,

$$10 = 4/3(27) + 4(9) + C$$

$$10 = 36 + 36 + C$$

$$C = 10 - 72$$

$$C = -62$$

Thus, the equation for y is:

$$y = 4/3x^3 + 4x^2 - 62$$

Let's do one last problem to give you a flavor for what the rest of calculus will be like. You now have the core of calculus, which is the derivative and the integral and their relationship. The rest of calculus will consist of rules and applications around this core. The next problem will demonstrate this. We first start with the rule as follows:

The Quotient Rule:

The quotient rule states that when you have a function over a function or equation, you do the following to solve the problem of taking the derivative. You basically take the top and perform the derivative then multiply by the bottom equation as is, then subtract the top times the bottom derivative all divided by the bottom squared. In formula fashion it looks like:

y = top/bottom, then

$$y' = \frac{\text{top}' \times \text{bottom} - \text{top} \times \text{bottom}'}{\text{bottom}^2}$$

Problem 15:

Find the derivative of $2x^4 / x^2$

Using the quotient rule,

$$y' = \frac{(2x^4)' \times (x^2) - (2x^4) \times (x^2)'}{(x^2)^2}$$

$$y' = \frac{(8x^3) \times (x^2) - (2x^4) \times (2x)}{(x^2)^2}$$

$$= \frac{8x^5 - 4x^5}{x^4}$$

$$= 4x$$

Derivation of derivative

As promised early in the section on calculus the derivation of derivative would be put forth. We will do this one last problem exercise so you will be prepared for class. When you see this derivation in the beginning of your calculus class, you will know where you are headed.

Remember we introduced the concept of limits early on in this section. Well now we will use this concept to develop the equation you have been using for derivative.

We will derive $f(x) = k(x^{k-1})$ the formula for derivative.

Here goes:

First, the initial definition of derivative was given as:

Let f(x) be a function.

Then $f'(x) = \lim_{\Delta x \to 0} (f(x + \Delta x) - f(x)) / \Delta x$

If this limit exists then f is differentiable and its derivative at x is $f'(x)$.

The best way to show this derivation is to do a problem:

Problem 16:

Find the derivative of $f(x) = x^3 + 2x$

Solution:

Using $k(x^{k-1})$ we get,

$$f' = 3x^2 + 2$$

Now let's go to the original formula for f'

$$f'(x) = \lim_{\Delta x \to 0} (f(x + \Delta x) - f(x)) / \Delta x$$

Let's plug in f(x)

$$f'(x) = \lim_{\Delta x \to 0} ((x + \Delta x)^3 + 2(x + \Delta x) - (x^3 + 2x)) / \Delta x$$

multiplying out the cube of $(x + \Delta x)^3$

$$= \lim_{\Delta x \to 0} (x^3 + 3x^2\Delta x + 3x(\Delta x)^2 + (\Delta x)^3 + 2x + 2\Delta x - x^3 - 2x) / \Delta x$$

simplifying

$$= \lim_{\Delta x \to 0} (3x^2\Delta x + 3x(\Delta x)^2 + (\Delta x)^3 + 2\Delta x) / \Delta x$$

factoring out Δx

$$= \lim_{\Delta x \to 0} (\Delta x(3x^2 + 3x\Delta x + (\Delta x)^2 + 2)) / \Delta x$$

crossing out Δx

$$= \lim_{\Delta x \to 0} (3x^2 + 3x\Delta x + (\Delta x)^2 + 2)$$

then as Δx becomes zero

$$f' = 3x^2 + 2$$

so we now know how our formula was derived through this problem.

There is a complete treatment of the derivation of the derivative that can be found on Wikibooks at:

http://en.wikibooks.org/wiki/Calculus/Differentiation/DifferentiationDefined

You will have this type of derivation in your calculus book. I didn't start out with the derivation as most books do because I wanted to emphasize the relationship of derivative calculus to integral calculus first.

Let's do one more problem with differentiation (derivative). It's a classic instantaneous velocity problem. Differentiation was made for this function.

Problem 17:

A particle is travelling at a velocity given by the time formula v = meters per second and is given as the function $4t^3 + 10t - 6$. V is in meters/second and t is in seconds. What is the instant velocity at time = 5 seconds?

Taking the derivative of $4t^3 + 10t - 6$ we get

$$12t^2 + 10$$

The instant velocity therefore at 5 seconds is 310 m/sec.

Graphing

Since functions can be graphed, be prepared to do some graphs. You will obviously require graph paper. It should be pointed out that derivatives and integrals can be "seen" on graphs. The derivative is a tangent to a point on the line and an integral is the area under the curve defined by the points on the integral symbol.

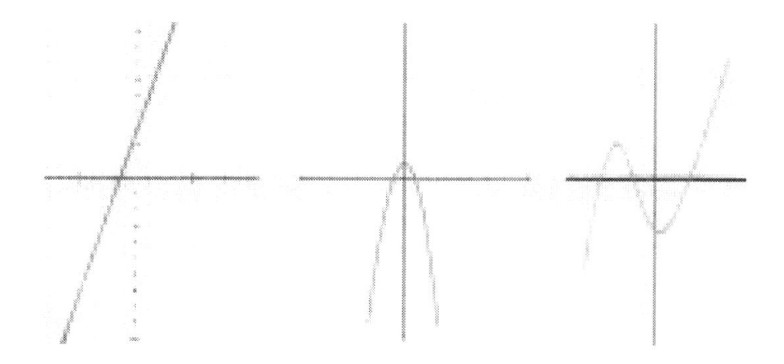

Calculus books use graphing to explain the concept and rules used in calculus. Many problems will require graphing as part of the answer.

Differentiation (derivative) and integration (integral) rules

This treatise on calculus has covered the heart of the subject and showed the main rules of both derivative and integral calculus. There are more rules for both. In fact, there are approximately 22 rules for differentiation and 18 for integration. Each of these will require explanation, proofing in some cases, and application understanding.

It is unlikely that any one calculus course could cover more than a few of these, but be aware there is a great deal of material for this discipline. Depending on what level of calculus you take, you will cover some of these.

Summary:

You now have a basic understanding of calculus. You now know what it is going to look like. Some of the examples or problems shown to you were very basic and only covered some of the applications of the tool of the derivative and the integral, which make up the course in calculus. School will fill in the spaces between the simple and complex with many applications and problems.

With practice, problem solving will become second nature. This overview will give you a leg up on doing well in calculus. The biggest thing is practice, practice, practice. Just like in real estate it is location, location, location. The methods and techniques described in this book will net you an A if followed. You need to know what formulas to use and how to apply them.

However, as discussed earlier you need to talk to your guidance counselor and make a decision whether calculus is the correct course to take for your career goals.

Remember, this country needs more of you to go into math and science. It's where the jobs are going to be created. It's where the world can be made a better place and it's where the United States can stand tall amongst the other nations. Calculus is a course that may or may not help you in your personal endeavor. It may be better to study old SAT or ACT tests and be prepared for these rather than take calculus. A solid SAT or ACT could mean the difference between a scholarship and no scholarship. And if your goal is to go into industry as a technical person, then it might be well to concentrate on chemistry and physics instead of spreading yourself thin with calculus. Only you can make this decision.

Best of luck and success to you,

John D. Forlini

Appendix A

Steps to Solve Word Problems:

1. First and foremost figure out what the problem wants from you. Sounds simple, but half the time this is where we fall down. Are they asking you for speed, numbers of kittens, or time. Whatever it is write it down and then give it a letter. For some reason most people like to use x. However, it is a great practice to use the letter that corresponds to what you are looking for.
2. Write down what units the answer should be in. Is it feet, square feet, or cubic feet, ohms, lumens, etc.
3. Ignore the unnecessary stuff in the word problem. Don't let stuff that is not essential confuse you.
4. If possible draw a picture that is representative of the question. Geometry and Trigonometry based questions lend themselves well to pictures.
5. Make a label (letter or number if given) for each item or variable.
6. Set up an equation or equations that satisfy the request and given information. Sometimes just putting the problems words into an equation will give you the guidance to solve the problem as will a good drawing.
7. Put the equation or equations into its simple easy form. Put all the letters on one side and the numbers on the other. If it's more than one equation, try to manipulate them to look alike. Sometimes this will mean that you don't have all the letters on one side and all the numbers on the right. You will have to play with it.
8. You will always hit that awful problem that you just can't see how to do. Don't waste time on this one, go to the next one. Remember on an ACT entrance exam or other exam most of the time every problem has equal weight. So put this one aside for later. The brain is an amazing entity. Sometimes while you are working on other problems, your brain will be unconsciously working out the solution to the problem in the background.
9. Check your work quickly by substituting your answer back into the original equation, if appropriate.

Note to Educators, Scientists, and Mathematicians:

Gentlemen and Ladies,

Your inputs would be sincerely appreciated. We all have a common objective to improve our youngsters' ability in math and science and improve our standing among the nations of the world.

As such, any suggested edit, improvement, and/or addition used would be incorporated on the next printing, which would be the next book ordered in the queue. The printing presses used for this book are digital and do not require the set up times of the past, thus it is a simple fix to add or modify to the next book in the queue.

Please address your inputs to 4linipublishing@charter.net. Your inputs will be credited to you in the book credits. Sending your inputs means that you are authorizing the publisher to freely use these in the book.

Thank you,

John D. Forlini

Made in the USA
Lexington, KY
10 May 2016